GourmetNutrition

THE COOKBOOK FOR THE FIT FOOD LOVER

GourmetNutrition

THE COOKBOOK FOR THE FIT FOOD LOVER

Dr. John M. Berardi,
Michael Williams & Kristina Andrew

DESIGN Seesaw Creative Communications, **seesawcreative.ca**
PHOTOGRAPHY Jason Grenci

Published by Precision Nutrition Inc.

Printed and bound in Canada. 03/12
Print management by Exodus Graphics Corp.

Acknowledgements

As always, a book like this can't exist without a nutritionally passionate, health conscious readership. So I'd like to begin by thanking every single *Gourmet Nutrition* reader and customer. Your continual demand for recipes that taste great and are great for you continues to inspire us in the kitchen.

Next, I'd like to thank the entire Precision Nutrition team. Your tireless efforts in helping to bring this book into existence continues to be appreciated.

Finally, I'd like to thank my friend and colleague, Dr. John Williams. Without your work on the first edition of *Gourmet Nutrition*, this book would never have come to be.

Dr. Berardi

Writing a book teaches you many things about yourself and how to rely on those around you. David Crow, you were there for us when our words needed flow. Tyler Jeal, Naomi Kolesnikoff and the Precision Nutrition team, thank you for your support in making this book great. Christophe Letard and Richard Norwood, your culinary influence is forever with us. Mom and Dad, thank you for your taste buds and for teaching us to be strong. John Riopka, your guidance has kept us together in the kitchen and in life. Patrick and Jill, your patience and friendship are immeasurable. And we have to thank each other for the inspiration, commitment and appreciation we share. Bon appetite!

Mike and Kristina

Special thanks also goes out to:

Carmelo Galati for his excellent design work.

Siobhan Kukolic and Rachael Bell for their editorial support.

Jason Grenci and Debbi Moses for their photography and food styling contributions.

Benjamin J. Gibson, Victoria Bolton, Douglas Ide, Jean Pritchett, Ji Jin Lim, Alex Rowson, Kim Keeling, and Laura Owen for their help with recipe testing and macronutrient calculation.

Contents

Recipes

1
Introduction

By Dr. John Berardi

Most people view food very simply: it either tastes good, or it's good for you – and never the two shall meet.

We at Precision Nutrition are on a mission to change that view. The book you now hold in your hands is proof positive that food can both be good and taste great at the same time.

And I want to be clear about one other thing: this is a book for people who want to look spectacular. Not just lose a few pounds here or there, not just drop an inch of the waist, or not just feel more "well" (whatever that means). *Gourmet Nutrition* is for people who want their bodies to look like fewer and fewer bodies actually look these days: stunning, healthy and strong.

As a nutrition researcher, coach and consultant for almost 15 years now, I've worked with thousands of clients around the world, everyone from Olympic athletes to cardiac patients, from people just getting started toward their goals to those who have been exercising and eating well for years.

And to this day, no matter who the audience, when I first present the revolutionary concept that you can eat great tasting food and still have a great-looking, healthy physique, laughter generally ensues.

The truth is that sometimes the old cliché is accurate; sometimes "health food" is just plain awful. And that drives some folks away from eating healthy altogether.

Others decide to lower their heads and keep at it, eating miserable tasting food in a brave attempt to lose weight or accomplish some other health or physique goal.

Neither group knows that there's a better way.

See, the whole "all healthy food tastes bad" thing is either a myth or just a lame excuse. Indeed, I can tell you with 100% certainty that there are many people who eat healthy meals every day – either to feel better, or look better, or get strong enough and fast enough to reach the outer limit of human performance – and they do it by eating great tasting food.

Yes, every day, there are people out there eating healthy, easy-to-make meals that could be found in gourmet restaurants. Meals that could impress the most discerning foodie. Meals that could fool a first date, a reluctant spouse, or picky-eating kids. Meals that just plain taste good. Meals that, when planned and eaten consistently, can improve and even completely transform your body.

And how do they do it? With Gourmet Nutrition.

Look, I've been there. I've eaten all that terrible food too. But at a certain point, it got tiresome. It got old. So insteac of trying to overcome the protests of a thousand unsatisfied taste buds, I decided to do something about it.

I sat down with my good friend and noted recipe maestro, Dr. John Williams, and created the ultimate physique-friendly cookbook, *Gourmet Nutrition*. Originally appearing as an e-book, *Gourmet Nutrition, Volume 1* instantly became an Internet best-seller. The feedback was exceptional. Yet there were two problems with *Gourmet Nutrition, Volume 1*.

First, it was an e-book. And people wanted it as a hardcopy, as an in-the-flesh book they could hold in their hands and lay flat on their counters while they cooked.

Second, *Gourmet Nutrition* readers wanted more. Once they worked through the first 100 great-tasting recipes, they wanted more *Gourmet Nutrition* meal ideas.

In response to these two requests, I decided to get back to work and create another volume of *Gourmet Nutrition*. This time I enlisted the help of gourmet chef, Michael Williams and his culinary counterpart Kristina Andrew. And among the three of us, we came up with over 100 additional *Gourmet Nutrition* recipes – each of them presented in this very book, a beautifully photographed hardcopy that's equally at home on the countertop and the coffee table.

What's a "Gourmet Nutrition" meal?

Now, at this point, you might be asking yourself – "There are a few thousand cookbooks on the market – so what makes *Gourmet Nutrition* so special?" Well, simply put: *Gourmet Nutrition* is where taste meets physiology.

You see, traditionally, the worlds of gourmet cooking and healthy nutrition have been at odds. The gourmands have sacrificed all (including nutritional value) at the altar of flavor and the artistic presentation of food. And the nutritionists have sacrificed all (including flavor) at the altar of physiology and nutritional value.

Yet flavor and nutritional value are not mutually exclusive. They are absolutely reconcilable. And with *Gourmet Nutrition*, we've created meals that taste great and are healthy too.

1. Must taste great

Simply put, to be considered for inclusion into this book, every meal was scrutinized by the discriminating palates of a number of chefs, nutritionists and foodies. And only those recipes with the highest ratings were included in *Gourmet Nutrition*.

2. Must contain lean, complete protein

Protein is the building block of muscle. And even if you don't want to build more muscle, you definitely want to preserve the muscle that you have for as long as you can. This helps to keep your metabolism revving, improve your weight loss profile, and reduce cardiovascular disease risk. And that's why we encourage you to eat a lean, complete protein source with each meal. Now, if all of this protein stuff is above your head, that's okay. We show you just how to do it with each and every *Gourmet Nutrition* meal option.

3. Must be low in sugar and processed carbohydrates

Sugar is not always the demon ingredient it's made out to be. But there are valid and strong reasons to limit sugar and processed carbohydrates in your diet. These types of carbohydrates digest too quickly, leading to erratic blood sugar, energy levels, and hormonal responses – none of which does your health or physique any favors. Therefore, each *Gourmet Nutrition* meal has been created in such a way as to help you limit the amount of sugar you take in each and every day.

4. Must prioritize healthy fats over bad fats

Whenever possible, the goal of every health-conscious individual should be to eliminate the nasty trans fat we hear so much about. But even beyond avoiding trans fats, it's important to keep our saturated fats in check while prioritizing healthy mono and polyunsaturated fats. *Gourmet Nutrition* makes this easy, as our meals eliminate trans fats while balancing out your saturates, monos and polyunsaturates – leaving the meal planning to us and the eating to you.

5. Must control calorie intake and density

One of the major reasons many people gain fat as they age (aside from lack of exercise) is the fact that their daily meals are often too high in calories. Indeed, many popular food choices can be quite calorie dense. And this means that even though you don't feel like you were eating a lot of food, you're packing in too many calories with each meal. To this end, we've designed *Gourmet Nutrition* to provide meals with a relatively low calorie density as well as variable portion sizes. This helps you avoid sneaking hundreds of extra calories into your diet unknowingly with each meal.

6. Must include fresh, natural, additive-free ingredients wherever possible

In general, the fresher the ingredient, the better it is for you. So, when choosing your meals, ask yourself if you've ever seen what you're about to eat growing in the ground or running around on a farm somewhere. If the answer is no, you're about to eat processed food. Ditto for anything that comes in a box or plastic container. Now, understand, it'll be next to impossible to avoid all processed foods. In fact, there may be some processed foods that you want to include in your diet. That's okay. Really, you just want to make sure that your daily diet draws mostly on fresh, whole foods. And the meals presented in *Gourmet Nutrition* can help you do this.

7. Must include carbs only if you deserve them

You've probably read all about high-carb vs. low-carb dieting. In my opinion, this high- vs. low-carb debate is a little misunderstood. As the body handles carbs best when it's in an exercised state, the best carb strategy is this: eat carbs only if you've earned them. Have you exercised? If so, you've earned a higher-carb meal. Have you exercised a lot? If so, you've earned even more carbs. However, keep this in mind: if you haven't exercised, your carb intake should be low. *Gourmet Nutrition* helps you keep track of this carb thing by separating meals into two categories – **post-workout** meals and **anytime** meals. More on this to follow.

Post-workout vs. Anytime meals

You'll notice that all the meals in this book are designated as either **post-workout** or **anytime** meals.

Note: this designation is listed right under the title of the recipe, so you'll be able to tell at a glance what type of meal it is.

Why does this classification exist? Well, research shows us that the body handles carbohydrates best immediately after exercise. From this, we know that it's a good idea to consume most of our daily carbohydrates within the 2-3 hour period after we exercise (post-workout). Likewise, if we haven't exercised, it's best to avoid higher-carb meals during this time – instead focusing on proteins, good fats and veggies. To this end:

Post-workout meals are those meals that contain a moderate to high amount of carbohydrates (greater than 26% carbohydrates). I recommend eating these meals within 2-3 hours of your last exercise session.

Anytime meals are those meals that contain a low amount of carbohydrates (less than 25% carbohydrates). I recommend eating these meals any other time outside of your post-workout period.

Please note that this rule is a general rule of thumb that works well for most as a starting point. Now, I should mention that some people are actually able to tolerate higher carbohydrate intakes outside of the period; that is, they can eat more pastas, breads, sugars and the like without getting fat. These individuals generally know who they are. They're often naturally very lean, and sometimes very skinny.

If you don't fit into that category, you're best off consuming carbs only in the 2-3 hours after an intense workout, or at least using that as the starting point for some trial and error, slowly introducing carbs outside that window and measuring the results.

Cooking instruction, *Gourmet Nutrition* style.

Okay, now that you've got an idea of what *Gourmet Nutrition* is all about, I should also mention that unlike most cookbooks, the books in the *Gourmet Nutrition* series aren't mere collections of recipes. Instead, they also teach you how to cook.

Indeed, rather than simply giving you list after list of ingredients, telling you how much of this, how long to cook that, what temperature to turn the oven dial to, and how to disconnect your smoke alarm before beginning, the *Gourmet Nutrition* books share with you the universal cooking principles so important to making great meals.

For example, in this volume, we'll share with you strategies for combining your main protein dishes with a variety of side dishes and homemade condiments for an almost unlimited number of meal creations. In doing this, the number of recipes available to you in this book increases from the 100 that were promised you, to a few hundred when all is said and done.

Further, we'll show you how you can make small changes to ingredient lists to magically turn anytime meals into post-workout meals and vice versa. You'll feel like Harry Houdini of the kitchen.

In addition, we'll also show you how to incorporate a variety of spices into different dishes to dramatically change the flavor palate. If you're a salt and pepper person, that's fine; you can stick with the basics. However, if you like to spice it up, we'll teach you how to use rosemary, cilantro, paprika, and more.

After spending some time with *Gourmet Nutrition*, no longer will you feel that twinge of insecurity when you enter the kitchen, wondering if you're going to end up with a really nice blackened swordfish or just a smoldering, blackened pan. This book aims to be your own personal cooking teacher and your own personal nutrition coach – all wrapped into one.

If you want more help...

Many of you reading this book already own the Precision Nutrition System; for those that don't, it's worth checking out.

The Precision Nutrition System is basically the mother of all dieting guides. If you really want to know what it takes to build a phenomenal body, everything from the physiology to the logistics, then the PN System is what you want. In it, I'll show you how to build your favorite *Gourmet Nutrition* meals into a complete meal plan that will deliver the results you're after. Plus, we include a copy of the original *Gourmet Nutrition* cookbook, so you'll get another 100 or so meal ideas too.

If you're reading this, I'm assuming you're probably not just eating for the heck of it. I'm guessing that you're trying to achieve something. You're trying to change your body to work the way you want it to work, to feel the way you want it to feel, to look the way you want it to look. To change your body, you need a plan. And that's where Precision Nutrition comes in.

So, while reading through this book, if you find yourself looking to learn more about how to integrate these great tasting, healthy *Gourmet Nutrition* meals into a complete nutrition plan, log on to **www.precisionnutrition.com** and check out what we have in store for you.

2

How to Use this Book

We've designed *Gourmet Nutrition* to be very easy to use, but also flexible and powerful enough to allow you to achieve whatever physique goals you may have, no matter how extraordinary. To make it both simple and powerful, we've adopted certain conventions and methods that are worth taking a few pages to explain.

Conventions used in *Gourmet Nutrition*

Large & Small Serving Sizes. Each recipe has both large and small serving sizes. The large serving sizes range from about 500 to 700 calories per serving, while the small serving sizes range from 200 to 400 calories per serving. In general, assuming you're eating every 2-3 hours during the day, the small serving size is a good starting point for women, while the large serving size is a good starting point for men.

Post-workout (Pw) **& anytime meals** (At). Post-workout meals have higher carbohydrate content and are best suited for the 3 hour period after exercise. Anytime meals can be eaten any other time of the day. Many recipes include instructions on how to alter the meal to change it from a post-workout meal to an anytime meal, or vice versa. See the "Variations and Options" at the bottom of each recipe for some examples.

Main + Side Pairings. To make this book as flexible as possible, and to encourage variety and creativity, we've come up with an easy way for you to make your own meals by pairing a main dish with either a post-workout or an anytime side. Each main dish recipe provides an example of both a PW and an AT pairing to get you started, but the following page shows a chart you can use to create some combinations of your own.

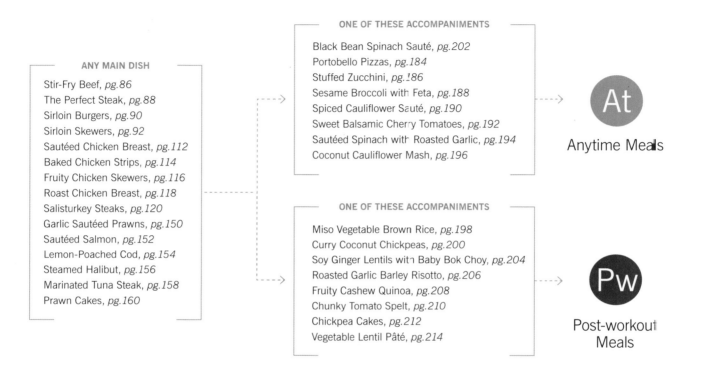

ANY MAIN DISH

Stir-Fry Beef, *pg.86*
The Perfect Steak, *pg.88*
Sirloin Burgers, *pg.90*
Sirloin Skewers, *pg.92*
Sautéed Chicken Breast, *pg.112*
Baked Chicken Strips, *pg.114*
Fruity Chicken Skewers, *pg.116*
Roast Chicken Breast, *pg.118*
Salisturkey Steaks, *pg.120*
Garlic Sautéed Prawns, *pg.150*
Sautéed Salmon, *pg.152*
Lemon-Poached Cod, *pg.154*
Steamed Halibut, *pg.156*
Marinated Tuna Steak, *pg.158*
Prawn Cakes, *pg.160*

ONE OF THESE ACCOMPANIMENTS

Black Bean Spinach Sauté, *pg.202*
Portobello Pizzas, *pg.184*
Stuffed Zucchini, *pg.186*
Sesame Broccoli with Feta, *pg.188*
Spiced Cauliflower Sauté, *pg.190*
Sweet Balsamic Cherry Tomatoes, *pg.192*
Sautéed Spinach with Roasted Garlic, *pg.194*
Coconut Cauliflower Mash, *pg.196*

At

Anytime Meals

ONE OF THESE ACCOMPANIMENTS

Miso Vegetable Brown Rice, *pg.198*
Curry Coconut Chickpeas, *pg.200*
Soy Ginger Lentils with Baby Bok Choy, *pg.204*
Roasted Garlic Barley Risotto, *pg.206*
Fruity Cashew Quinoa, *pg.208*
Chunky Tomato Spelt, *pg.210*
Chickpea Cakes, *pg.212*
Vegetable Lentil Pâté, *pg.214*

Pw

Post-workout Meals

How to build a meal plan

If you already own the Precision Nutrition System, building an optimal plan from these new *Gourmet Nutrition* meals is straightforward. If however you're just starting out, here's a short primer on how to get the most out of this book.

Basically, there are three ways you could use *Gourmet Nutrition* to build a better body for yourself. Here I call them "levels," the first of which is both very simple and highly effective, and the last of which is the most challenging but also the closest you can get to a "perfect diet" as modern science will allow.

Level 1:

Eat a Gourmet Nutrition meal every 2 -3 hours. (Easy; 90th Percentile)

The easiest way to use this book is to simply eat any one of these meals every 2-3 hours you're awake. A simple method, but by doing that alone you'll be eating better than 90% of the population. Why?

- Proper meal frequency
- Protein in every meal
- Controlled carbohydrate intake

- Good balance of healthy fats
- Ample fruit and vegetable intake
- Good starting point for total calories per day

You hear these things talked about often, but rarely do you see a practical way of doing it all at the same time. That's the beauty of this book: it's been designed so that if all you ever did was eat a *Gourmet Nutrition* meal – any *Gourmet Nutrition meal* – every 2 to 3 hours you're awake, you'd be doing all those things without even thinking of them. And if you do all those things, while exercising regularly, you'll inevitably lose some fat, build some lean muscle, and feel better than ever before.

Level 2:

Eat carbs only if you deserve them. (Moderate; 95th Percentile)

Level 2 is the same as Level 1, but with one twist: you eat the meals marked "post-workout" only in the 3 hours after you've exercised. The rest of the meals you eat in the day would be "anytime" meals. This is another simple change that requires only moderately more effort, yet yields significant results when you look in the mirror. Make that change and you'll be eating better – and ultimately, looking better – than 95 percent of the population.

The reason is that organizing your meals this way allows you to make use of the concept of "nutrient timing." The science is complex, but the basic idea is to consume carbs in and around the workout period, when they are better tolerated by the body. In this case, "better tolerated" essentially means "less likely to be stored as fat." That's desirable, as I'm sure you'll agree.

As I mentioned earlier, the "post-workout" meals (PW) tend to have slightly higher carbohydrate content, while the "anytime" meals (AT) tend to have lower carbohydrate content and focus instead on lean protein, vegetables and healthy fats. So by simply eating the PW meals in the 3 hours after you've exercised and the AT meals the rest of the time, all the hard work is done for you.

On the following pages are 4 examples of what such a plan might look like, based on whether or not you've exercised as well as your daily exercise time:

Gourmet Nutrition Meal Template – **Non-Exercise Days**

MEAL	MEAL CHOICES	CUSTOMIZATION FOR YOU	EXAMPLE MEALS (Fill in yourself)
Breakfast	Any meal from *Gourmet Nutrition* that's categorized as (At)	**Men** 1 large serving **Women** 1 small serving	
Snack	Any shake or snack from *Gourmet Nutrition* that's categorized as (At)	**Men** 1 large serving **Women** 1 small serving	
Lunch	Any meal from *Gourmet Nutrition* that's categorized as (At)	**Men** 1 large serving **Women** 1 small serving	
Snack	Any shake or snack from *Gourmet Nutrition* that's categorized as (At)	**Men** 1 large serving **Women** 1 small serving	
Dinner	Any meal from *Gourmet Nutrition* that's categorized as (At)	**Men** 1 large serving **Women** 1 small serving	

Gourmet Nutrition Meal Template – **Morning Workout**

MEAL	MEAL CHOICES	CUSTOMIZATION FOR YOU	EXAMPLE MEALS (Fill in yourself)
	EXERCISE Sip a protein/carbohydrate-rich workout drink during exercise		
Breakfast	Any meal from *Gourmet Nutrition* that's categorized as (Pw)	**Men** 1 large serving **Women** 1 small serving	
Snack	Any shake or snack from *Gourmet Nutrition* that's categorized as (At)	**Men** 1 large serving **Women** 1 small serving	
Lunch	Any meal from *Gourmet Nutrition* that's categorized as (At)	**Men** 1 large serving **Women** 1 small serving	
Snack	Any shake or snack from *Gourmet Nutrition* that's categorized as (At)	**Men** 1 large serving **Women** 1 small serving	
Dinner	Any meal from *Gourmet Nutrition* that's categorized as (At)	**Men** 1 large serving **Women** 1 small serving	

Gourmet Nutrition Meal Template – **Afternoon Workout**

MEAL	MEAL CHOICES	CUSTOMIZATION FOR YOU	EXAMPLE MEALS (Fill in yourself)
Breakfast	Any meal from *Gourmet Nutrition* that's categorized as At	**Men** 1 large serving **Women** 1 small serving	
Snack	Any shake or snack from *Gourmet Nutrition* that's categorized as At	**Men** 1 large serving **Women** 1 small serving	
EXERCISE Sip a protein/carbohydrate-rich workout drink during exercise			
Lunch	Any meal from Gourmet Nutrition that's categorized as Pw	**Men** 1 large serving **Women** 1 small serving	
Snack	Any shake or snack from *Gourmet Nutrition* that's categorized as At	**Men** 1 large serving **Women** 1 small serving	
Dinner	Any meal from *Gourmet Nutrition* that's categorized as At	**Men** 1 large serving **Women** 1 small serving	

Gourmet Nutrition Meal Template – **Evening Workout**

MEAL	MEAL CHOICES	CUSTOMIZATION FOR YOU	EXAMPLE MEALS (Fill in yourself)
Breakfast	Any meal from *Gourmet Nutrition* that's categorized as (At)	**Men** 1 large serving **Women** 1 small serving	
Snack	Any shake or snack from *Gourmet Nutrition* that's categorized as (At)	**Men** 1 large serving **Women** 1 small serving	
Lunch	Any meal from *Gourmet Nutrition* that's categorized as (At)	**Men** 1 large serving **Women** 1 small serving	
Snack	Any shake or snack from *Gourmet Nutrition* that's categorized as (At)	**Men** 1 large serving **Women** 1 small serving	
EXERCISE Sip a protein/carbohydrate-rich workout drink during exercise			
Dinner	Any meal from *Gourmet Nutrition* that's categorized as (Pw)	**Men** 1 large serving **Women** 1 small serving	

Eating this way really simplifies the decision-making process. Haven't worked out today? No high-carb meals for you! Want to eat that pasta, or even have that dessert? Get your butt to the gym first! In the end, it keeps you accountable and pegs your carb intake to the amount of exercise you do, both of which are very good things.

In the end, you'll end up eating higher-carb meals only when you deserve them – that is, once you've put your time in at the gym! Your body will thank you for it.

Level 3:

Individualize and optimize your plan. (Challenging; 99% Percentile)

Level 3 is for people who want to push their own limits and get in the kind of shape they've never been in before.

The way to do that is to create a customized meal plan for yourself that takes into account the various factors that differentiate you from your neighbors; namely, your body type, your current body composition and your goals, among many other things.

The second part of the process is then to optimize that plan over time by measuring and quantifying your results. How you do so depends entirely on your goals: if you want to lose fat, then periodic body composition testing is in order; if you want to improve your cardiovascular health, you would measure your blood lipids; if you wanted to improve your recovery and stress management, you might regularly take a Profile of Mood States questionnaire. Whatever your goals, you would choose one or more quantifiable metrics and track them on a regular basis.

The third part is to alter your plan if those metrics don't show any measurable progress toward your goals. This is what we call "optimization." For example, in the Precision Nutrition System, we include an entire *Diet Guide* to explain this process and show you exactly what alterations to make and when.

Doing this process justice in a few short pages is impossible; that said, it's important to understand why a standard cookie-cutter diet will not yield extraordinary results.

1. Your body and physiology are unique, so your meal plan must take that into account. The DNA of any two people may be 99.9% similar, the remaining 0.1% can make all the difference in the world.

2. Your goals are different. Some people want to lose fat, others want to build muscle, others want to run marathons or run a faster 40-yard dash. Those goals are quite different and require very different meal plans.

3. Finding the perfect diet for you is an iterative process. Right now there is no way of instantaneously knowing the perfect diet for any individual. But you can arrive at a perfect diet using a scientific approach over a period of time, usually about 4 to 6 months.

I say that this level is "challenging," but in reality it's still quite simple. Eating this way is however somewhat more involved and requires a certain focus and commitment, and therefore it's generally suited to people who are willing to make their bodies the first priority in their lives for a little while. Typically this includes people who are either frustrated by past dieting attempts or those who are generally satisfied with their current physique but are looking to go that much further.

We cover all this in the Precision Nutrition System, so if you're interested in joining the 99th percentile, pick up a copy at **www.precisionnutrition.com**

3

General Cooking Rules & Tips

Right from the start, we'd like to tell you that unlike most cookbooks, this isn't just a collection of recipes. This book will also teach you how to cook, rather than simply give you list after list of ingredients, tell you how much of this, how long to cook that, what temperature to turn the oven dial to and how to disconnect your smoke alarm before beginning (yes, it happens to everyone).

While providing itemized meal ideas to help you achieve your ideal body, we will also be concentrating on providing you with the knowledge and ability to create your own recipes and helping make life in your kitchen simple, fun, and full of enjoyment. When it comes down to it, this book aims to be your own personal cooking teacher.

In our kitchen at home, regardless of whether we are cooking just for ourselves or preparing a four-course lesson for 35 people, we try to always follow a number of rules. (Trust us, the more you follow these, the easier things will be for you.) Here they are:

Go big

Always try to cook large batches of meals, then portion into meal sizes. If you refrigerate or freeze a number of extra meals each time you cook, you will always have healthy and delicious food on hand.

Be prepared

When cooking, always prepare whatever you can in advance. This, of course, is vitally important whenever we have a large lesson or catering event, but it also makes the cooking we do as part of our everyday routine much easier.

At the beginning of the week, sit down and try to imagine what you want to cook for the upcoming 7 days. Then, you can buy everything in a single trip to the grocery store, instead of going every day just to pick up odds and ends. Again, this will free up more time for you. By avoiding 5 needless visits to the grocery store, you save yourself an extra 3 hours a week.

Once home from the store, set up shop in the kitchen and get most of your preparation done for the entire week in one go. All of your veggies can be sliced and refrigerated in plastic containers (don't worry, we'll explain all about slicing and dicing later in the book, along with some helpful tricks the professional chefs use). You can cook up large portions of grains and make a month's supply of your healthy soups, sauces or salad dressings. As we all know, social interaction is very important for maintaining a healthy lifestyle, so why don't you try to make this into a cooperative event with family, friends or even children. (And that means less work for you, right?)

Get it from the best

When buying your ingredients, try to purchase from organic and local suppliers, as close to home as possible. The quality and freshness to be found at such suppliers will be far superior and, trust us, both the taste and price will surprise you! We also strongly believe in supporting our community's small businesses as our way of giving back. Look up your local farmer's markets and find a neighborhood butcher if one is available.

Remember, cooking is fun!

In your cooking, don't be afraid to experiment or try the different variations we have provided in the recipes, or even some of your own. We used a wide variety of common and some not-so-common foods. If you don't like a certain ingredient or it isn't available at your local market, simply substitute with something else that you think might benefit the dish. After all, that's the way the professional chefs do it and, remember, our recipes teach you to cook, not to follow a recipe blindly. The principles and techniques that you get from this book are far more important than the recipes themselves. This is something that develops with time, but be patient and it will come. Just remember to have fun. If something doesn't work at first, don't get discouraged. In cooking, accidents are often a blessing in disguise, as this is how better and new recipes are discovered. (In fact, a few of the recipes featured in this book started out as mistakes... but, of course, we aren't going to tell you which ones.)

So that's it for our principles of cooking. Now it's time to get into the main stuff. In the following pages, you will be given what we informally call our "Cooking 101" lesson. The common (and not so common) cooking terms that will be used in the remainder of the book will be explained. You will be given a suggested equipment and pantry list and step-by-step instructions on how we set up our kitchen. Then, there is a daily prep list, and basic directions on how to prepare your veggies and starches. And finally, we're off to the races... it's time to cook!

Food Preparation Tips

The following are some general tips that you'll want to keep in mind when shopping for and cooking the meals outlined in *Gourmet Nutrition*.

Place a wet rag beneath your cutting board to prevent it from slipping.

Have a large plastic container close at hand to use as a garbage bin for all of your veggie ends or wrappings. This saves time and keeps your floor clean compared to running to and from your full-size kitchen garbage bin.

All of the tools you will need (knives, peelers, pots, utensils, etc.) should be laid out and easily accessible.

Same thing goes for your ingredients, including oils and spices. Laying everything out is key and that is what makes the process go so quickly.

Keep tasting spoons, measuring spoons and utensils clean by leaving them in a container filled with warm water; this will keep your countertop cleaner.

Extra storage containers and wet rags for cleaning should be out and ready to use. If you tidy as you go and stay organized, the whole process will be much easier on your kitchen.

Your sink should be full of hot, soapy water. This way you can wash dishes as you use them or at least soak them as you go.

Before you get started, read the whole recipe over, including the variations and options. Always know the next step before you get to it.

Blending hot liquids should be done with extreme caution. Only fill the blender half full, put the lid on just before blending, and start on low and work up to high. When removing the lid lift it away from you.

When you add meats and vegetables to a preheated pan, the pan should produce a sizzling sound. If it doesn't, next time make sure you let it preheat a little longer.

You will notice in most of our recipes we add the spices to the frying pan and heat them; this helps bring out their flavor.

We have suggested measurements for spices including salt and pepper; however, this is something that is extremely sensitive to personal taste, so we encourage you to add spices to taste and use the suggestions as guidelines only.

Garlic and ginger burn easily and turn bitter, so watch them carefully and stir constantly.

When preheating a pan, do this without oil in it; otherwise the oil will burn.

Use butter or coconut oil when cooking because these two oils have a higher smoke point (the temperature at which oils smoke and begin to break down) and it is not good to consume oils that are heated beyond their smoke points.

Some oils will solidify when cooled. If this happens, you can heat them for 5-10 seconds in a microwave or leave them out at room temperature (this will be the case for some of our salad dressings).

Use unrefined or virgin oil sprays whenever possible to reduce the number of calories and cooked oil you consume.

Canned beans should be rinsed and drained in a strainer before using.

We've mentioned this a couple of times and will probably do so again because it's extremely important: whenever possible, pay attention to the variations and options for storage suggestions and cook in large batches. This is especially true for soups, salad dressings, protein and grains. Remember, double or triple batches are always great for leftovers.

The easiest way to double or triple a recipe is to simply use the same measurement twice or three times, respectively. For example, if you want to double a recipe that calls for ½ cup of onions, then just add two ½ cups of onions. To triple a recipe, do the same thing but add three portions. For example, if a recipes calls for ⅛ teaspoon of pepper, add three ⅛ teaspoons. Simple enough!

To increase the life of a non-stick frying pan, only use it up to medium heat, wait until the pan is cooled before washing it, and only ever use heat-resistant plastic utensils in it.

Buy your canned items in water or natural juices. Foods canned in either oil or syrup will be adding unnecessary calories and preservatives to your food.

Buy produce in season whenever possible, as seasonal produce will not only have a better nutritional profile and be noticeably sweeter, but will also be cheaper.

When writing a shopping list, group items according to their location in the grocery store or market (i.e. produce, bulk, frozen, deli, butcher, dairy, canned). If you have time to go to a local butcher for your meats and fish, a farmer's market for produce, and a grocery store for everything else, divide your lists accordingly.

Minimize clutter. Spring cleaning is just as essential in the kitchen as it is in the rest of the house – and it's not just for spring! If you haven't used something (food or equipment) in the past two months it shouldn't be in the kitchen. After all, no one will ever know if you throw out that cool gizmo they gave you for your birthday or as a wedding present.

Keep the equipment and foods you use accessible and not put away in a cupboard somewhere. Kitchens are to be used, not to be looked at.

Organize your kitchen like a grocery store. Similar items should be stored in proximity to each other. Keep spices with spices, nuts with nuts, uncooked grains and legumes together, vegetables with vegetables and fruits with fruits.

Tools & Equipment

One of the first things that our cooking lesson clients mention is how much easier cooking can be when they are using our equipment. Therefore, we have compiled a list of items that we think are essential, because having the right equipment truly does make a world of difference in the kitchen. Through our experience, we have seen the best and worst of everyday kitchen equipment and with all the gimmicks out there, we've come up with a simple list and some shopping pointers.

Essentials

Chef's Knife (8-inch) and Paring Knife (4-inch)
A full tang (when the blade goes all the way through the handle) will give the knife balance and strength, a heavy bolster will give the knife some weight, making it easier to use, and a forged blade will hold its point and sharpness longer. (Just ask about these at any kitchen supply store; they'll know what you are talking about.)

Cutting Board Either plastic or wood is good, but if you go with a wood board, make sure there are no joints. Eventually the joints will separate and this creates a breeding ground for bacteria. Avoid glass boards as they will dull your knives quickly.

Non-Stick Frying Pan (10 inches) Look for a high-quality non-stick pan (not Teflon) with a heavy bottom (for good heat distribution) and a heat-resistant handle.

Large Pot (5 liters or 5 quarts or larger) and Small Pot (1 liter or 1 quart) Again, a heavy bottom will heat the pot more evenly and prevent hot spots from developing (which may cause warping). 18/10 stainless steel with an aluminum or copper encapsulated core is best.

Blender Multi-speed, high-quality, minimum 1.5 liters or 1.5 quarts. These are great for both smoothies and soups.

Mini Food Processor This will make your life far easier when preparing salad dressings, crushing nuts, mincing garlic, blending condiments or finely chopping vegetables.

Heat-Resistant Plastic Flipper Make sure it is quite rigid or else it will be difficult to lift large quantities.

Heat-Resistant Spatula These come in a variety of sizes; choose whichever one meets your needs.

Storage Containers Try to get a variety of sizes, either plastic or glass, with tight-fitting lids.

Mixing Bowls (Large and Small) Plastic or metal, quite deep, with upright (instead of angled) edges and a flat bottom.

Measuring Cups 1 cup, ¾ cup, ½ cup, ⅓ cup and ¼ cup.

Large Measuring Cup A 2 or 4 cup size will give you better accuracy when measuring larger quantities (and save you time).

Measuring Spoons 1 tablespoon, 1 teaspoon, ½ teaspoon, ¼ teaspoon and ⅛ teaspoon.

Cheese Grater Four-sided box-style works best.

Vegetable Peeler European Y-shaped one.

Baking Pans Non-stick, 9" x 13" rectangular or 9" x 9" square pan.

Kitchen Cloths Highly absorbent, thick.

Optional

Large Salad Spinner Bigger is better; push tops are easier to use than the pull-string varieties, and; a flat top makes for easier storage.

Cookie Sheet Stainless steel with a reflective layer for even browning.

Spice Rack or Carousel If all your spices are easily accessible, in one place and in alphabetical order, you are more likely to use them.

Coffee Grinder This will also be used for grinding spices.

Tongs Look for ones with a strong spring (the more resistance you feel when you close the tongs the better) and heat-resistant plastic tips so you can use them in your non-stick frying pan.

Strainer Minimum 2 liters or 2 quarts.

Pantry List

Here's a list of the most common items you'll need on hand when preparing most of the GN recipes. Note that for some recipes you may need other ingredients not included on these lists. However, with these on hand, your grocery trips will be significantly quicker and easier.

The importance of having a fully stocked pantry reminds us of a story. While we were working on writing this cookbook, a friend of ours stopped by one evening and asked us if we could give him the recipe for granola. As we told him what ingredients he would need, we quickly realized it would be easier for us to make it, as he didn't know if he even had half of the basic ingredients like oats and cinnamon. We were able to whip him up a batch of granola right there on the spot with dried fruit, coconut and nuts without having to make a trip to the grocery store. He was amazed how easy cooking could be when you had all the ingredients at hand. Take note: if you make an effort to purchase items in bulk when they are on sale, you can save a lot of time, a lot of stress, and a lot of money.

Miscellaneous Items

Coconut milk
(avoid light versions)

Unpasteurized honey

Pure vanilla extract

Organic soy sauce
(Tamari)

Miso paste (Shiro)

Mix of dried fruit

Canned pumpkin
(avoid pumpkin
pie filling)

Organic, low-sodium
vegetable, beef and
chicken broths

Vinegars

Red wine

Balsamic

Apple cider

Rice wine

Spices

Cinnamon

Chili powder

Curry powder

Coriander

Cumin

Fennel

Nutmeg

Paprika

Pepper

Sea salt

Turmeric

(Whenever possible,
buy whole spices and
grind as needed.)

Grains

Spelt

Quinoa

Large flake whole oats

Barley (pot or pearled)

Brown rice (medium
grain)

Nuts and Seeds

Walnuts

Almonds

Pecans

Cashews

Pumpkin seeds

Sunflower seeds

Sesame seeds
(black or white)

Lentils and Beans
(organic canned or
uncooked)

French green lentils

Red lentils

Navy beans

Black beans

Kidney beans

Chickpeas/garbanzo
beans

Frozen Fruits

Blueberries

Strawberries

Raspberries

Blackberries

Oils

Olive

Coconut

Sesame

Flaxseed
(store in fridge)

Fish (store in fridge)

(Whenever possible,
purchase extra virgin,
cold-pressed or
unrefined oils)

Preparation List

Vegetables/Fruits

Apples Slice the apple in half, then into quarters right through the middle of the fruit (from the stem down). Lay the apple on one side and make a single angled cut (this is much easier than holding the apple and trying to make a u-shaped cut around the core). From there, cut the remaining pieces into whatever size is necessary for the recipe.

Asparagus Assemble the stalks together in a bunch and make sure all the bottoms are in line. Cut off the bottom white part (approximately 1-2 inches). Sometimes that's all that is necessary; other recipes call for the asparagus to be then sliced lengthwise or in sections.

Avocado Holding the avocado in the palm of one hand, cut lengthwise into it until the knife meets the pit. Then, carefully turn the avocado around the knife until you have a single cut all the way around, twist the two halves in opposite directions and pull apart. Cut firmly into the pit and use the knife to remove it from the flesh. With a small spoon, separate the flesh from the rind and then either mash or dice as needed.

Beets Wearing disposable or plastic gloves if you have them, cut the top and bottom off of the beet. Then peel the skin of the beet with a vegetable peeler. Cut the beet into whatever size is necessary for the recipe. Remember to wash your cutting board immediately to prevent beet stains.

Broccoli For large florets, simply break off from the main piece. For smaller florets, cut the stem right at the base where the florets meet the stalk. If desired, the remaining stalk can then be diced.

Cabbage Cut the cabbage into quarters (sometimes it will already be cut by the grocer). Then, with an angled cut at the base, remove the core (the fibrous part where it was attached to the plant). The cabbage can then either be shredded (use the large-bore side of the grater) or chopped (approximately one-inch square pieces are best).

Cauliflower See Broccoli.

Cucumber See Zucchini.

Fennel Bulb Cut the fennel into quarters. Then, with an angled cut, remove the core (the fibrous part where it was attached to the plant). Now you can either finely slice or dice depending on your needs. Follow the instructions on dicing and slicing onions.

Garlic Cut both the bottom and the top off of a whole head (bulb). Separate the cloves and remove as much of the skin as possible. Using the side of your chef's knife, press the knife firmly down on each clove with your other hand until it pops (the clove, not your hand). The remaining pieces of skin should then be easily discarded. The garlic can then either be finely diced or minced using a food processor. If making big batches, which we recommend, stir in some extra virgin olive oil to help preserve it.

Ginger It is a good idea to store ginger in the freezer. We simply cut any blemishes or rough edges off the ginger and then freeze. Then, it is amazingly simple to grate using the finest side of your grater. (It is not even necessary to remove any of the skin first.)

Kiwi Cut the kiwi in half and scoop out the flesh with a small spoon. It can then be either diced or blended, whatever the recipe asks for.

Mushrooms For regular brown or button mushrooms, place the cap down on the cutting board and use your knife to slice in approximately $\frac{1}{8}$ inch slices, which can then be chopped further if necessary. Portobello mushrooms need to first have the stem removed. Hold the stem firmly and twist. Using a small spoon, remove the gills from the inside of the cap. Run the spoon against the natural grain of the gills.

Olives Buy them pre-pitted if possible. If not, using your thumbnail or a pairing knife, cut the olive until you meet the pit. Expose and remove.

Onion To dice the onion, cut away the top and bottom of the onion tip and root, slice it in half from tip to root and peel away the outside shell (this will also get rid of the skin). Place one half of the onion cut side down with the root end facing towards your non-cutting hand with your non-cutting hand on top, parallel with the cutting board. Lightly hold the onion in place with the palm of your hand with your fingers outstretched and out of the way. Starting about

$\frac{1}{2}$ inch up from the cutting board, make a horizontal incision $\frac{3}{4}$ of the way through the onion. Make additional horizontal incisions every $\frac{1}{2}$ inch (the onion should still be intact). Turn the onion 90° and place your fingertips on top of the onion, pushing your knuckles forward (your knuckles will act as a guide for the knife keeping your precious fingertips out of the way). With your knife perpendicular to the previous incisions make a set of vertical slices from left to right approximately $\frac{1}{2}$ inch apart. Turn the onion 90° again to make the final cuts, which will produce the diced pieces of onion. The remaining piece is difficult to hold, so lay it flat and dice it up using your knuckles to guide the knife. Repeat for the remaining half. To make small or finely diced onion, make the horizontal and vertical incisions closer together.

To slice the onion, cut away the top and bottom tip and root of the onion, slice it in half from tip to root and peel away the outside shell (this will also get rid of the skin). Peel away two layers of the onion at one time and lay flat on the cutting board. Press your hand firmly on top of the layers (this will cause them to break and lay completely flat). Holding the onion layers with your fingertips and pushing your knuckles forward to use as a guide, make a series of vertical slices from right to left for righties and left to right for lefties. To make finely sliced onion, make the slices as close together as you can.

When it comes to crying while cutting onions, we're still working on it. Some of our clients have suggested placing the onion under cold running water just before preparation (this sacrifices some flavor) or chilling the onions in a fridge (doesn't work as well).

Orange Cut off the top and bottom of the orange. To remove the peel and underlying white layer, use a series of slices. Place orange on cutting board cut end down. Hold the orange on top with your non-cutting hand. Cut down and away along the contour of the orange. Once the orange is completely peeled, cut lengthwise in quarters and cut away the interior core of the orange (as we did with the apples). Seeded oranges will then need to have their seeds removed. From there you can either slice or dice into whatever size pieces the recipe indicates.

Peppers Cut the pepper in half (through the stem). The stem, white membrane and seeds should be easily pulled out. For sliced peppers, place the skin side of the pepper down on your cutting board and after cutting away the top and bottom of the pepper, slice very thin lengthwise strips (about $\frac{1}{8}$ inch wide). For diced peppers, cut thicker slices (about $\frac{1}{2}$ inch), then turn 90° and slice the pieces into 1 inch segments.

Spinach Leaving the spinach tied together, cut the stems of spinach where they meet the leaves. You will then be left with mostly leaves. Rip away the remaining stems by hand (don't cut the spinach as it will wilt more quickly), wash the leaves in a bowl (or sink) of cold water, then spin them dry in your salad spinner. Make sure to remove as much water as possible, as this ensures maximum life expectancy for your spinach.

Squash Cut the squash lengthwise in half. With a large spoon, scoop out the seeds. The squash can now be roasted in the oven, cooled and then the flesh scooped from the skin. For diced squash, peel the skin (with acorn squash, you can leave some skin on) and then slice (skin side down) and dice into about 1 inch square pieces for roasting or whatever the recipe calls for.

Sweet potato Peel the sweet potato with your Y-shaped vegetable peeler. Cut away the top and bottom. For cubed (diced) pieces, make lengthwise slices about $\frac{1}{2}$ inch apart. Lay two of the slices on the cutting board on top of each other and make one or two lengthwise slices. Dice into $\frac{1}{2}$ inch square pieces from there. To slice, cut the potato in half lengthwise and lay the cut sides down on a cutting board. Holding the potato with your fingertips and pushing your knuckles forward to use as a guide, make a series of slices from one end to the other approximately $\frac{1}{4}$ - $\frac{1}{2}$ inch apart.

Tomato With the core on one side of your knife, cut the tomato in half (you will end up with one half slightly larger than the other). A small pair of cuts in the shape of a 'V' should then remove the core. With the tomato halves skin side down (to avoid fighting the skin), cut each half into approximately four segments. Then turn 90° and dice or slice the tomato as needed.

Yams See Sweet potato.

Zucchini Cut away both ends of the zucchini. Holding the zucchini firmly in place, slice it in half lengthwise and lay both halves on the cutting board cut side down. For slices, slice from one end to the other with desired thickness. For dices, cut in half again lengthwise. Without moving the zucchini, cut into pieces a ½ inch apart from one end to the other.

Grains/Legumes

Barley Pre-rinse. Use a ratio of 2:1 for liquid to barley. Bring liquid to a boil on high heat, add barley and cover. Cook for 25 minutes on medium-low. Drain any excess water.

Brown rice (medium grain) Pre-rinse. Use a ratio of 2:1 for liquid to rice. Bring liquid to a boil on high heat, add rice and cover. Cook 50 minutes on medium-low. Drain any excess water.

Lentils, french green Pre-rinse. Use a ratio of 3:1 for liquid to lentils. Bring liquid to a boil on high heat, add lentils and cover. Cook 25 minutes on medium-low, drain excess water.

Lentils, orange/red Pre-rinse. Use a ratio of 3:1 for liquid to lentils. Bring liquid to a boil on high heat, add lentils and cover. Cook 5 minutes on medium, drain excess water.

Oats Do not pre-rinse. Use a ratio of 2:1 for liquid to oats. Bring liquid to a boil on high heat, add oats and cover. Cook 8-10 minutes on medium-low until water is absorbed.

Quinoa Pre-rinse. Use a ratio of 2:1 for liquid to quinoa. Bring liquid to a boil on high heat, add quinoa and cover. Cook 10 minutes on low, remove from heat and let sit covered for 10 minutes.

Spelt Soak over night in water. In the morning drain water. Use a ratio of 2:1 for liquid to spelt. Bring liquid to a boil and add spelt. Cook 50-60 minutes on medium-low, drain excess water.

Herbs

Basil Stack a number of basil leaves (about 3 or 4) and roll them lengthwise into a tight bundle. Starting at one end and proceeding to the other, chop the bundle into very small pieces. Be sure that your knife is slicing through the basil rather than simply crushing it into the cutting board.

Cilantro Wash and dry. Then holding the bunched cilantro by the stems, shave away the leaves with your knife (it is necessary to have a very sharp knife for the process). Discard the stem, and pick out any small remaining pieces of stem by hand. Then pull the leaves together into a loose pile and chop into fine pieces. It's very important that the cilantro is dry when chopping

Mint See Basil.

Parsley See Cilantro.

Rosemary Pulling against the grain of the rosemary, use your fingers to remove the rosemary 'needles' from the spine. The needles can then be finely chopped.

Spices

Cumin Add three tablespoons to a coffee grinder and grind into a powdery mixture.

Coriander Add three tablespoons to a coffee grinder and grind into a powdery mixture.

Fennel seed Add three tablespoons to a coffee grinder and grind into a powdery mixture.

Pepper Add three tablespoons to a coffee grinder and grind into a powdery mixture.

Nuts

An easy way to chop/crush nuts is to place them in a plastic bag and use a heavy saucepan as a hammer. (It's a great way to relieve built-up stress, too!)

Meats/Poultry/Seafood

- Store in an airtight container

- Store in the back of the fridge or freezer to prevent temperature change when the door is opened

- Once defrosted do not refreeze

- Cooking extends refrigerated life but shortens frozen life

Ground Beef

Raw stores up to 2 days refrigerated and up to 4 months frozen

Cooked stores up to 4 days refrigerated and up to 3 months frozen

Steak

Raw stores up to 3 days refrigerated and up to 10 months frozen

Cooked stores up to 5 days refrigerated and up to 3 months frozen

Burgers

Raw stores up to 2 days refrigerated and up to 4 months frozen

Cooked stores up to 4 days refrigerated and up to 3 months frozen

Chicken

Raw stores up to 2 days refrigerated and up to 9 months frozen

Cooked stores up to 4 days refrigerated and up to 4 months frozen

Shrimp/Prawns/Scallops

Raw stores up to 2 days refrigerated and up to 6 months frozen

Cooked stores up to 4 days refrigerated and up to 3 months frozen

Lean Fish

Raw stores 1-2 days refrigerated and up to 6 months frozen

Cooked stores up to 4 days refrigerated and up to 6 months frozen

Fatty Fish

Raw stores 1-2 days refrigerated and up to 3 months frozen

Cooked stores up to 4 days refrigerated and up to 6 months frozen

Turkey Sausage

Raw stores 1-2 days refrigerated and up to 2 months frozen

Cooked stores up to 4 days refrigerated and up to 3 months frozen

4

Breakfast

Breakfast, as the saying goes, is the most important meal of the day. Emerging from its slumber, your body is begging you to end the fast. And it's your job to provide high-quality nutrition to begin the day on the right foot.

In this breakfast section, you'll find a number of delicious oatmeal recipes, tasty egg recipes, and even a few other breakfast delights that are sure to please.

Keep in mind that these breakfasts aren't just for the morning. They can be eaten any time of day. Our oatmeal recipes, for example, are perfect meals to eat after exercise, and they even taste great when cold. Break conventions – nothing is set in stone. Get creative and experiment; instead of plain water in your oatmeal, try herbal teas or freshly squeezed juices. And since oatmeal by itself is very low in protein, remember to add some protein powder, yogurt and/or cottage cheese.

Even if you don't have a lot of time in the mornings, you can still enjoy these recipes. Try making them the night before and reheating when you wake up. Frittatas, eggs and quiches can even be made on the weekends, frozen, and enjoyed later. Defrosting in the fridge over night or in the microwave in the morning allows for a quick and painless breakfast. These ideas may seem almost sacrilegious, but if you're in a rush, you're much better off defrosting a breakfast than choosing a coffee and donut – or skipping breakfast altogether.

Remember, breakfast is the first chance you get to fuel your body and your brain for the day. So make your breakfast count.

Maple Walnut Apple Oatmeal

Pw
Post-workout
Meal

5 min.
Preparation
Time

10 min.
Cooking
Time

Nutritional Information

(per serving)	large	small
Calories (k/cal)	619.2	309.6
Fat (g)	23.5	11.8
Saturated (g)	2.4	1.2
Monounsaturated (g)	3.5	1.7
Polyunsaturated (g)	14.8	7.4
omega-3 (g)	2.9	1.5
omega-6 (g)	1.9	1.0
Carbohydrates (g)	63.6	31.8
fiber (g)	8.4	4.2
sugars (g)	26.0	13.0
Protein (g)	38.3	19.2

Maple syrup is a breakfast favorite – although when served atop a stack of flapjacks, the sugar and carb content climbs while the nutritional profile takes a nose-dive. In this physique-friendly breakfast, maple syrup, walnuts and apples complement a protein-packed bowl of oats.

Instructions

Bring ½ a cup of water and milk to a boil in a small pot on medium heat. Add the oats and cinnamon. Reduce heat to medium-low and simmer until liquid is absorbed (approximately 7-10 minutes), stirring occasionally. Remove from heat and mix in apples, walnuts and maple syrup. Combine ¼ cup of water with whey protein in a separate bowl. Mix with a fork until protein is dissolved. For a smoother consistency, pour protein mixture into a blender or food processor and blend until protein is dissolved. Pour protein mixture over oatmeal and serve. **Serves 1 large or 2 small.**

Water	**½ cup**
Low-fat milk	**½ cup**
Old fashioned large flake oats	**½ cup**
Cinnamon	**½ tsp**
Apple (cored and cut into small pieces)	**½**
Crushed walnuts	**¼ cup**
100% pure maple syrup	**1 tbsp**
Water	**¼ cup**
Vanilla whey protein (equal to 25 g protein)	**1 scoop**

Variations and Options

If you like your oatmeal softer, add 2-4 tablespoons of extra water to the pot before adding the oats and cinnamon. **If you are lactose intolerant or would prefer not to use milk, omit ½ cup of low-fat milk and replace with ½ cup of water and ½ scoop of protein powder. Alternatively, you can substitute with non-cow's-milk dairy (e.g. goat's milk).** Try substituting cinnamon with nutmeg for a different flavor. **For a creamier mixture, instead of mixing the whey protein with ¼ cup of water, try combining the protein with ¼ cup of apple sauce or yogurt.**

Chai Blueberry Oatmeal

Pw
Post-workout Meal

3 min. — Preparation Time

10 min. — Cooking Time

Nutritional Information

(per serving)	large	small
Calories (k/cal)	472.3	236.1
Fat (g)	10.2	5.1
Saturated (g)	1.0	0.5
Monounsaturated (g)	1.9	0.9
Polyunsaturated (g)	5.0	2.5
omega-3 (g)	3.4	1.7
omega-6 (g)	1.6	0.8
Carbohydrates (g)	60.7	30.4
fiber(g)	9.7	4.9
sugars (g)	24.8	12.4
Protein (g)	34.5	17.2

Chai is the word for tea in South Asia and the Middle East, while in English, chai refers specifically to spiced tea. Chai's spices, which usually include one or more of the following: cardamom, cinnamon, ginger, star anise, peppercorn and cloves, lend this tea a strong scent and flavor. Coupled with the sweetness of berries, vanilla protein and honey, as well as the goodness of oats, this breakfast offers a slow-digesting, sensory morning bouquet.

Instructions

Bring 1¼ cups of water to a boil in a small pot on high heat. Remove from heat and steep a chai tea bag for 5 minutes. Remove bag and bring back to a boil. Add the oats. Reduce heat to medium-low and simmer until liquid is absorbed (approximately 7-10 minutes), stirring occasionally. Remove from heat and stir in flax seeds and honey. Combine ¼ cup of milk with whey protein in a separate bowl. Mix with a fork until protein is dissolved. For a smoother consistency, pour protein mixture into a blender or food processor and blend until protein is dissolved. Pour protein mixture and blueberries over oatmeal and serve. **Serves 1 large or 2 small.**

Water	1¼ cups
Chai tea	1 bag
Old fashioned large flake oats	½ cup
Flax seeds (ground)	2 tbsp
100% Pure honey	1 tbsp
Low-fat milk	¼ cup
Vanilla whey protein (equal to 25 g protein)	1 scoop
Blueberries (fresh or frozen)	¼ cup

Variations and Options

If you like your oatmeal softer, add 2-4 tablespoons of extra water to the pot before making the tea. **If you are lactose intolerant or would prefer not to use milk, omit ¼ cup of low-fat milk and replace with ¼ cup of water and ½ scoop of protein powder or ¼ cup of soy milk.** Alternatively, you can substitute with non-cow's-milk dairy (e.g. goat's milk). Substitute ½ cup of blueberries with ¼ cup of sliced banana for a different flavor. **For chocolate chai flavor, omit blueberries and substitute vanilla protein powder with chocolate protein powder.**

Orangealicious Oatmeal

Pw

Post-workout
Meal

5 min.
Preparation
Time

10 min.
Cooking
Time

Nutritional Information

(per serving)	large	small
Calories (k/cal)	530.9	265.4
Fat (g)	18.2	9.1
Saturated (g)	1.8	0.9
Monounsaturated (g)	3.7	1.8
Polyunsaturated (g)	10.1	5.0
omega-3 (g)	7.5	3.8
omega-6 (g)	2.5	1.3
Carbohydrates (g)	57.5	28.7
fiber (g)	7.0	3.5
sugars (g)	22.6	11.3
Protein (g)	34.4	17.2

Most people enjoy a cup of morning orange juice. However, orange juice alone leaves too much to be desired in terms of its nutritional profile. So instead of going with the orange juice alone, why not add your orange juice and some fresh oranges to a delicious bowl of oatmeal? If you're a fan of oranges, be sure to try this protein-rich Orangealicious addition to your breakfast table.

Instructions

In a small pot bring water and orange juice to a boil on high heat. Add the oats. Reduce heat to medium-low and simmer until liquid is absorbed (approximately 7-10 minutes), stirring occasionally. Remove from heat and mix in oranges and oil. Combine ¼ cup of yogurt with whey protein in a separate bowl. Mix with a fork until protein is dissolved. Pour protein mixture over oatmeal and serve. **Serves 1 large or 2 small.**

Water	½ cup
Orange juice	½ cup
Old fashioned large flake oats	½ cup
Orange (cut into small pieces)	½
Flaxseed oil	1 tbsp
Plain low-fat yogurt	¼ cup
Vanilla whey protein (equal to 25 g protein)	1 scoop

Variations and Options

If you like your oatmeal softer, add 2-4 tablespoons of extra water to the pot before adding oats. **If you are lactose intolerant or wish to avoid dairy, replace the ¼ cup of yogurt with either ¼ cup of soy yogurt or ¼ cup of water and ½ scoop of protein powder. Alternatively, you can substitute with non-cow's-milk dairy (e.g. goat's milk).** For chocolate orange oatmeal, instead of mixing vanilla whey protein with ¼ cup of water, combine the same amount of protein powder with ¼ cup of low-fat chocolate milk. **To save time in the morning, you can make your oatmeal the night before and eat it chilled in the morning. However, don't add the protein mixture until the morning.**

Banana Cream Pie Oatmeal

Pw

Post-workout
Meal

3 min.

Preparation
Time

10 min.

Cooking
Time

Nutritional Information

(per serving)	large	small
Calories (k/cal)	523.1	261.6
Fat (g)	16.7	8.3
Saturated (g)	11.5	5.7
Monounsaturated (g)	1.4	0.7
Polyunsaturated (g)	1.2	0.6
omega-3 (g)	0.3	0.1
omega-6 (g)	0.9	0.5
Carbohydrates (g)	53.9	26.9
fiber (g)	6.1	3.1
sugars (g)	14.0	7.0
Protein (g)	39.4	19.7

This recipe combines fresh bananas and coconut milk – a beverage made from the meat of mature coconut. Packed with anti-viral, anti-bacterial, and anti-fungal agents, coconut milk is not only delicious; it's also very good for you. If you like the taste of piña coladas, you'll love this oatmeal recipe.

Instructions

In a small pot bring milk and coconut milk to a boil over medium heat. Add the oats. Reduce heat to medium-low and simmer until milk is absorbed (approximately 7-10 minutes), stirring occasionally. Combine ¼ cup of water with whey protein in a separate bowl. Mix with a fork until protein is dissolved. For a smoother consistency, mix powder with water in blender or food processor and blend until protein is dissolved. Pour protein mixture and bananas over oatmeal and serve. **Serves 1 large or 2 small.**

Low-fat milk	1 cup
Coconut milk	¼ cup
Old fashioned large flake oats	½ cup
Water	¼ cup
Vanilla whey protein (equal to 25 g protein)	1 scoop
Banana (sliced)	½

Variations and Options

If you like your oatmeal softer, add 2-4 tablespoons of extra water to the pot before adding oats. **If you are lactose intolerant or wish to avoid dairy, replace the 1 cup of milk with 1 cup of water and ½ scoop of protein powder. Alternatively, you can substitute with non-cow's-milk dairy (e.g. goat's milk, yogurt).** For a creamier mixture, instead of mixing the whey protein with ¼ cup of water, try combining the protein with ¼ cup of apple sauce or yogurt. **If you'd like your oatmeal to be infused with banana flavor, add ½ cup of mashed banana once the oatmeal has simmered for 5 minutes. Then continue to cook for an additional 2 minutes or so.**

Pumpkin Pie Oatmeal

5 min.
Preparation Time

10 min.
Cooking Time

Post-workout Meal

Nutritional Information

(per serving)	large	small
Calories (k/cal)	575.0	287.5
Fat (g)	22.7	11.4
Saturated (g)	2.1	1.0
Monounsaturated (g)	12.5	6.3
Polyunsaturated (g)	5.4	2.7
omega-3 (g)	0.3	0.1
omega-6 (g)	5.1	2.6
Carbohydrates (g)	50.5	25.3
fiber (g)	12.1	6.1
sugars (g)	10.6	5.3
Protein (g)	42.0	21.0

Not only is pumpkin a delicious dietary addition, it contains a synergistic blend of phytonutrients, rich in carotenoids. But that's no reason to eat high-sugar pumpkin pie! Instead, try our Pumpkin Pie Oatmeal. This delicious pumpkin recipe is a great breakfast treat, full of slow digesting carbs and healthy fats.

Instructions

In a small pot bring milk and water to a boil over medium heat. Add the oats, cinnamon and nutmeg. Reduce heat to medium-low and simmer until liquid is absorbed (approximately 7-10 minutes), stirring occasionally. Once liquid is absorbed, stir in pumpkin, almonds and Splenda® and set aside. Combine ¼ cup of water with whey protein in a separate bowl. Mix with a fork until protein is dissolved. For a smoother consistency, mix powder with water in blender or food processor and blend until protein is dissolved. Pour protein mixture over oatmeal and serve. **Serves 1 large or 2 small.**

Low-fat milk	**½ cup**
Water	**¾ cup**
Old fashioned large flake oats	**½ cup**
Cinnamon	**1 pinch**
Nutmeg	**1 pinch**
Pumpkin (canned)	**¼ cup**
Almonds (sliced)	**¼ cup**
Splenda®, to taste	
Water	**¼ cup**
Vanilla whey protein (equal to 25 g protein)	**1 scoop**

Variations and Options

If you like your oatmeal softer, add 2-4 tablespoons of extra water to the pot before adding oats. **If you are lactose intolerant or wish to avoid dairy, replace the ½ cup of milk with ½ cup of water and ½ scoop of protein powder. Alternatively, you can substitute with non-cow's-milk dairy (e.g. goat's milk, yogurt).** For a creamier mixture, instead of mixing whey protein with ¼ cup of water, combine protein with ¼ cup of yogurt and pour over oatmeal. **For a fall treat, you can also substitute almonds with roasted pumpkin seeds.** If you'd like to avoid Splenda®, you can replace with a small amount of stevia.

Eggs Benedict with Sautéed Onion

At

Anytime
Meal

10 min.
Preparation Time

20 min.
Cooking Time

Nutritional Information

(per serving)	large	small
Calories (k/cal)	687.0	229.0
Fat (g)	38.1	12.7
Saturated (g)	13.6	4.5
Monounsaturated (g)	10.6	3.5
Polyunsaturated (g)	9.5	3.2
omega-3 (g)	2.0	0.7
omega-6 (g)	7.7	2.6
Carbohydrates (g)	20.2	6.7
fiber (g)	2.8	0.9
sugars (g)	10.5	3.5
Protein (g)	66.0	22.0

TIP: The onion slices are in place of an English muffin, so it's important not to break them.

Eggs benedict is a high-carb, high-fat breakfast tradition – delicious but not so friendly to the waistline. So with this recipe, we've decided to cut the carbs, replacing the English muffin with sautéed onion slices. We also decided to cut the fat with a low-fat hollandaise sauce. The net result is a veggie-packed breakfast that's not only delicious; it's nutritious too.

Instructions

Preheat a non-stick frying pan on medium heat. Lightly coat with spray and gently place the 3 whole onion slices in the pan. Cook until the bottom is nicely browned and then gently flip each slice. Cook until onion is nicely browned on both sides. Carefully remove from pan and set aside. While the onions are cooking, whisk all hollandaise sauce ingredients together in a mixing bowl. Add mixture to a small saucepan and gently heat until mixture is warm but not boiling, and set aside. Once onions are done, re-spray pan and add the spinach. Cook until spinach shrinks to at least half its original size. Remove from pan and set aside. Place three onion slices individually on a plate. Put a tomato slice on top of each onion slice. Place ⅓ of the chicken, spinach and cheese on top of each onion slice. Top with an egg and garnish with hollandaise sauce. **Serves 1 large or 3 small.**

Eggs Benedict

Olive oil cooking spray	
Whole onion slices (¼ inch thick each)	3
Smoked chicken breast low-fat deli meat (140 g)	5 oz
Spinach	3 cups
Tomato	3 slices
Parmesan cheese (grated)	1.5 oz
Whole omega-3 eggs (individually poached or fried)	3

Hollandaise Sauce

Low-fat mayonnaise	2 tbsp
Plain low-fat yogurt	⅓ cup
Lemon juice	½ tsp
Dijon mustard	⅛ tsp
Salt	1 pinch
Splenda®	1 pinch
Chili powder	1 pinch

Variations and Options

Pw option: Add two slices of whole grain toast or any *Gourmet Nutrition* oatmeal recipe to the meal. **For a meat variation, substitute chicken with 2 oz (70 g) of lox or 5 oz (140 g) of turkey ham.** For a cheese variation, substitute parmesan cheese with slices of havarti or aged white cheddar. **For a veggie variation, substitute the spinach and tomato with other vegetables such as sautéed mushrooms, zucchini or red peppers.** For a sauce variation, replace hollandaise sauce with fresh pesto. **If you'd like to avoid Splenda®, you can replace with a small amount of stevia.**

Green Cuisine Frittata

5 min.
Preparation Time

10 min.
Cooking Time

Anytime Meal

Nutritional Information

(per serving)	large	small
Calories (k/cal)	467.9	234.0
Fat (g)	25.3	12.7
Saturated (g)	8.9	4.5
Monounsaturated (g)	7.7	3.9
Polyunsaturated (g)	7.9	4.0
omega-3 (g)	0.6	0.3
omega-6 (g)	6.2	3.1
Carbohydrates (g)	12.6	6.3
fiber (g)	3.6	1.8
sugars (g)	3.5	1.8
Protein (g)	47.4	23.7

TIP: With a spatula, lift a portion of the egg, allowing the runny egg on top to flow beneath the part that you lifted. Repeat this step three or four times at different spots.

A frittata is a type of Italian omelet that frequently features fillings such as meats, cheeses and vegetables – making it a great way to get all your breakfast nutrients in one simple dish. In this Green Cuisine Frittata, a host of fresh and frozen veggies are added to a fantastic feta cheese and ham omelet. The feta adds a creamy zest while the pumpkin seeds add a nice textured crunch. This is one breakfast omelet you're sure to love.

Instructions

Whisk egg whites, eggs, salt and pepper together in a mixing bowl. Preheat a large non-stick frying pan (with a heat-resistant handle) on medium heat. Lightly coat with spray. Add spinach and sauté for 10-30 seconds, stirring frequently. Add the pumpkin seeds, broccoli, peas, zucchini, onion and garlic. Sauté for 1 minute. Evenly pour the egg mixture over the vegetables in the pan. Cook for a couple of minutes until the top of the mixture begins to bubble. Evenly spread the cheese and ham on top of the frittata. Turn oven on to broil. Place pan in oven until egg is cooked (approximately 2-5 minutes). Remove from the oven, place onto a plate and serve. **Serves 2 large or 4 small.**

Egg whites (6 large)	1 cup
Whole omega-3 eggs	2
Salt	1 pinch
Pepper	1 pinch
Olive oil cooking spray	
Spinach	2 cups
Pumpkin seeds	¼ cup
Broccoli florets (small)	¼ cup
Peas (frozen or canned)	¼ cup
Zucchini (small diced)	¼ cup
Green onion (small diced)	¼ cup
Garlic (minced)	2 tsp
Low-fat feta cheese (crumbled)	½ cup
Turkey ham deli meat (large diced)	4 oz

Variations and Options

(Pw) option: Add two slices of whole grain toast or any *Gourmet Nutrition* oatmeal recipe to the meal. **For veggie variety, substitute the vegetables in this recipe with your favorites or whatever is in season.** For a different spice combination, try adding ¼ teaspoon of chili powder, ¼ teaspoon of cumin, ¼ teaspoon of salt and a pinch of pepper before whisking the egg mixture.

Breakfast Quiches

At Anytime Meal

5-8 min.
Preparation Time

20 min.
Cooking Time

Nutritional Information

(per serving)	large	small
Calories (k/cal)	569.4	284.7
Fat (g)	15.8	7.9
Saturated (g)	6.4	3.2
Monounsaturated (g)	4.9	2.5
Polyunsaturated (g)	2.0	1.0
omega-3 (g)	0.5	0.3
omega-6 (g)	1.1	0.5
Carbohydrates (g)	33.0	16.5
fiber (g)	8.0	4.0
sugars (g)	19.4	9.7
Protein (g)	73.8	36.9

TIP: As a quick check, try gently pressing the center of one of the quiches. If no liquid comes out, they should be ready.

In French cuisine, a quiche is a baked dish made primarily with eggs and milk or cream in a pastry crust. Typically high in calories, carbs and fats, the quiche is a rich and decadent meal that leads to a physique of Rubenesque proportions. Unless, that is, you're eating a low-fat, low-carb quiche. Rich in protein and veggies, these quiches, topped with a little salsa or pesto, are sure to bring a breakfast smile.

Instructions

Preheat the oven to 400°F. Add all ingredients to a blender except the salsa. Blend well on low. Lightly coat a non-stick muffin tray with spray. Evenly distribute mixture into each muffin cup, filling each half way. This will allow room for the mixture to rise when baking. Avoid using the foam and try to distribute the liquid, cheese, meat and vegetables evenly. Bake until egg is cooked all the way through (approximately 20 minutes). Remove from oven and cool. They will shrink, but don't be alarmed. To remove quiches from muffin cups, slide spoon along entire circular muffin cup edge and then lift. Serve with salsa and enjoy. **Serves 1 large or 2 small. (Makes about 12 quiche muffins.)**

Spinach	2 cups
Red pepper (rough chopped)	¼ cup
Onion (rough chopped)	¼ cup
Egg whites (6 large)	1 cup
Whole omega-3 eggs	2
Low-fat swiss cheese (grated)	¼ cup
Low-fat turkey deli meat (140 g)	5 oz
Garlic (rough chopped)	3 cloves
Cinnamon	¼ tsp
Olive oil cooking spray	
Salsa	½ cup

Variations and Options

These are amazing snacks when you're on the go and they taste great cold. You can make up a double or triple batch and freeze them. Take out a serving the night before and defrost in the fridge. Reheat in the oven or microwave. **Pw option: Add two slices of whole grain toast or any** *Gourmet Nutrition* **oatmeal recipe to the meal.** For veggie variety, substitute the vegetables in this recipe with your favorites or whatever is in season. Mushrooms, zucchini and broccoli work very well. **For a cheese variety, low-fat feta or aged white cheddar are great substitutes for swiss. You can even add a teaspoon of grated cheese, such as parmesan, to the top of the quiches before you put them in the oven.**

Peaches and Cream Omelet

Anytime Meal

3 min.
Preparation Time

10 min.
Cooking Time

Nutritional Information

(per serving)	large	small
Calories (k/cal)	651.8	325.9
Fat (g)	31.7	15.9
Saturated (g)	5.6	2.8
Monounsaturated (g)	14.6	7.3
Polyunsaturated (g)	8.1	4.0
omega-3 (g)	1.1	0.5
omega-6 (g)	7.2	3.6
Carbohydrates (g)	33.0	16.5
fiber (g)	5.2	2.6
sugars (g)	28.2	14.1
Protein (g)	58.6	29.3

TIP: With a spatula, lift a portion of the egg, allowing the runny egg on top to flow beneath the part that you lifted. Repeat this step three or four times at different spots.

It's no surprise that the heavenly taste of peaches and cream makes for a dessert classic. However, typical peaches and cream recipes are filled with sugar and fat. With this fresh take on peaches and cream, we've combined the goodness of peaches and cream with the protein power of a morning omelet. Not a combination most would think of – but this recipe is delicious in its unconventionality.

Instructions

Preheat a large non-stick frying pan on medium heat. Lightly coat with spray. Whisk egg whites, eggs, cinnamon and Splenda® together in a mixing bowl. Pour mixture into the pan. Cook for a couple of minutes until the top of the mixture begins to bubble. Cook for 1 minute until bottom is golden brown. Flip the omelet and cook until the other side is golden brown. Transfer omelet to a plate. Mix cottage cheese, peaches and pecans together and place half of the mixture onto one side of the omelet. Fold the omelet over to cover contents. Use remaining peach mixture as a fruit salad side, and garnish omelet with yogurt and serve. **Serves 1 large or 2 small.**

Olive oil cooking spray	
Egg whites (6 large)	**1 cup**
Whole omega-3 eggs	**2**
Cinnamon	**¹⁄₈ tsp**
Splenda® (1 package)	**¼ tsp**
Low-fat cottage cheese	**½ cup**
Small peaches (small diced)	**2**
Pecans (crushed)	**¼ cup**
Low-fat plain yogurt	**½ cup**

Rancher's Omelet

5 min.
Preparation Time

10 min.
Cooking Time

Anytime Meal

Nutritional Information

(per serving)	large	small
Calories (k/cal)	552.4	276.2
Fat (g)	25.7	12.9
Saturated (g)	9.0	4.5
Monounsaturated (g)	7.7	3.8
Polyunsaturated (g)	7.6	3.8
omega-3 (g)	0.9	0.5
omega-6 (g)	2.3	1.2
Carbohydrates (g)	16.6	8.3
fiber (g)	3.5	1.7
sugars (g)	9.4	4.7
Protein (g)	63.6	31.8

TIP: With a spatula, lift a portion of the egg, allowing the runny egg on top to flow beneath the part that you lifted. Repeat this step three or four times at different spots.

If you're looking for a hearty, no-nonsense breakfast, look no further than the Rancher's Omelet. Full of lean proteins and veggies, this omelet is a great morning kick-start – even if you don't have cattle to tend.

Instructions

Cook turkey sausage (refer to instructions on page 146) and then dice it. Preheat a large non-stick frying pan on medium heat. Lightly coat with spray. Add red pepper and onion. Sauté until onions are lightly browned, stirring frequently. Add cooked sausage, tomato and garlic and sauté for one minute more. Remove from pan and set aside. Whisk egg whites, eggs, salt and pepper together in a mixing bowl. Re-spray pan if needed and pour egg mixture into the pan. Cook until the top of the mixture begins to bubble and the bottom is golden brown. Flip the omelet and cook until the other side is golden brown. Transfer omelet to a plate. Place havarti cheese onto one half of the omelet and the vegetable and sausage mixture on top of the cheese. Fold the omelet over to cover contents. Garnish with salsa and serve. **Serves 1 large or 2 small.**

Turkey sausage (85 g)	3 oz
Olive oil cooking spray	
Red pepper (small diced)	¼ cup
Onion (small diced)	¼ cup
Tomato (small diced)	¼ cup
Garlic (minced)	1 tsp
Egg whites (6 large)	1 cup
Whole omega-3 eggs	2
Salt	¼ tsp
Pepper	pinch
Light havarti cheese (sliced, 28 g)	1 oz
Salsa	¼ cup

Variations and Options

 option: Add two slices of whole grain toast or any *Gourmet Nutrition* oatmeal recipe to the meal. **For some veggie variety, substitute the vegetables in this recipe with your favorites or whatever is in season.** If you don't want to smell like garlic, substitute garlic with 1 teaspoon of minced or grated ginger. **To switch from an omelet to a frittata, cook the omelet similar to how you'd cook a frittata. Refer to instructions on page 48.**

Tomato Salmon Scramble

At
Anytime Meal

5 min.
Preparation Time

10 min.
Cooking Time

If you find yourself getting a bit bored with your breakfast omelets, try this scramble on for size. It lends the unique flavors of omega-3- rich salmon, micronutrient-rich spinach, and Italian parsley, making for an exciting and health-promoting breakfast creation.

Nutritional Information

(per serving)	large	small
Calories (k/cal)	480.9	240.5
Fat (g)	20.0	10.0
Saturated (g)	4.5	2.3
Monounsaturated (g)	7.1	3.5
Polyunsaturated (g)	7.0	3.5
omega-3 (g)	1.3	0.7
omega-6 (g)	0.6	0.3
Carbohydrates (g)	11.2	5.6
fiber (g)	3.6	1.8
sugars (g)	6.4	3.2
Protein (g)	64.1	32.1

Instructions

Sauté salmon (refer to instructions on page 152). Remove skin if necessary, cut into 1 inch cubes and set aside. Preheat a non-stick frying pan on medium heat and lightly coat with spray. Add the spinach and sauté for 30 seconds. Add the tomatoes and mushrooms and sauté for 3-4 minutes more. Remove from heat and set mixture aside. Whisk egg whites, eggs, salt and pepper together in a mixing bowl. Return empty frying pan to medium heat. Lightly coat with spray and pour egg mixture into pan. Stir constantly to break up the egg. Once all the egg is cooked, add the sautéed salmon, parsley and vegetable mixture and breakfast is ready to enjoy.

Serves 1 large or 2 small.

Salmon (140 g)	5 oz
Olive oil cooking spray	
Fresh spinach	2 cups
Small tomatoes (rough chopped)	2
Mushrooms (rough chopped)	1 cup
Egg whites (6 large)	1 cup
Whole omega-3 eggs	2
Salt	¼ tsp
Pepper	1 pinch
Italian parsley (rough chopped)	1 tbsp

Variations and Options

Pw option: Add two slices of whole grain toast to the meal or make this a breakfast wrap by using whole grain tortilla shells. **For meat variety, substitute salmon with your favorite low-fat deli meat, turkey sausage or prawns.** To add some cheesy zest, garnish this scramble with 2 tablespoons of your favorite cheese or ¼ cup of feta. **To add a strong veggie twist, add ¼ cup of rehydrated sundried tomatoes.** For seasoning variety, spice up the egg scramble with a little chili powder or paprika.

Turkey Sausage and Yam Hash Browns

Post-workout Meal

5 min.
Preparation Time

10 min.
Cooking Time

If you're looking for a great breakfast alternative to eggs, look no further. Complete with lean turkey sausage, carotene-rich yams, and just the right combination of herbs and spices, this meal can serve as a delicious breakfast, lunch or dinner.

Nutritional Information

(per serving)	large	small
Calories (k/cal)	568.9	284.5
Fat (g)	29.5	14.7
Saturated (g)	11.1	5.6
Monounsaturated (g)	8.2	4.1
Polyunsaturated (g)	5.1	2.5
omega-3 (g)	0.3	0.1
omega-6 (g)	4.4	2.2
Carbohydrates (g)	32.1	16.1
fiber (g)	5.5	2.7
sugars (g)	8.1	4.0
Protein (g)	43.8	21.9

Instructions

Cook turkey sausage (refer to instructions on page 146). While the sausage is cooking, preheat a large non-stick frying pan on medium heat. Add water, turnip and yams. Cover and simmer for 10 minutes. Drain water and return to heat. Add butter and sauté until nicely browned. Add garlic, cinnamon, salt, pepper and paprika and cook for 1 minute more. Serve turkey sausage and hash browns together on a plate. **Serves 1 large or 2 small.**

Turkey sausage (170 g)	**6 oz**
Water	**1 cup**
Turnip (medium diced)	**½ cup**
Yams (medium diced)	**1 cup**
Butter	**1 tbsp**
Fresh garlic (minced)	**1 tsp**
Cinnamon	**⅛ tsp**
Salt	**⅛ tsp**
Pepper	**1 pinch**
Paprika	**1 pinch**

Variations and Options

At option: Use half the amount of yam and turnip to reduce the carb count. **To save some time, cook the sausage and hash brown mixture in the evening and reheat in the morning.** To make one big breakfast skillet, dice the turkey sausage and add it to the hash browns. Then garnish with 2 tablespoons of your favorite cheese. **To add some spice variety, add in 1 tablespoon of cilantro, rosemary or Italian parsley along with the paprika.** The old cliché potato versus patato has resurfaced when it comes to differentiating between sweet potatoes and yams. For the purposes of this recipe, we are referring to the yams that have orange flesh. However, for some variety, we encourage you to experiment and use a mixture of sweet potatoes, yams, parsnips or even squash.

Sunrise Sundae with French Toast Hash Browns

Pw

Post-workout
Meal

15 min.
Preparation Time

15 min.
Cooking Time

Nutritional Information

(per serving)	large	small
Calories (k/cal)	731.1	365.6
Fat (g)	33.1	16.6
Saturated (g)	7.1	3.6
Monounsaturated (g)	17.5	8.8
Polyunsaturated (g)	6.1	3.1
omega-3 (g)	0.3	0.2
omega-6 (g)	5.3	2.7
Carbohydrates (g)	59.6	29.8
fiber (g)	10.2	5.1
sugars (g)	24.1	12.1
Protein (g)	48.7	24.3

Let's face it, if you're at all physique-conscious, you've likely given up french toast a long time ago. However, with the help of some whole grain bread and omega-3 eggs, french toast is back on the menu. And this time it's served alongside a delicious, fruity ice-cream-free sundae. If you're looking for an awesome morning post-workout meal, look no further than the Sunrise Sundae.

Instructions

Sunrise Sundae Place all of the apple pieces in the bottom of a tall glass or bowl. Place the remaining ingredients on top of the apple in the order they appear in the ingredient list.

French Toast Cut bread into 1-inch square cubes. Whisk egg, cinnamon and salt in a small mixing bowl and place bread cubes into egg. Let soak for 30 seconds. Preheat a non-stick frying pan and lightly coat with spray. Pour the egg and bread mixture into the pan. Mixing as little as possible, lightly brown the bread. Remove from heat and serve. **Serves 1 large or 2 small.**

Sunrise Sundae

Apple (small diced)	¼ cup
Low-fat cottage cheese	½ cup
Nectarine (small diced)	¼ cup
Low-fat plain yogurt	¼ cup
Strawberry (sliced)	¼ cup
Low-fat cottage cheese	½ cup
Grapes	¼ cup
Mixed nuts (unsalted, crushed)	⅓ cup

French Toast

Whole grain bread	1 slice
Whole omega-3 egg	1
Cinnamon	pinch
Salt	pinch
Olive oil cooking spray	

Variations and Options

For fruit variety, substitute apple, strawberries, grapes and nectarine with your favorite fruits or whatever is in season. Banana, mango, peach, blueberries and melon are some of our favorites. **To add a vanilla taste to your Sunrise Sundae, mix your yogurt and cottage cheese with some vanilla protein powder before adding to the sundae.**

5

Shakes & Smoothies

Eating healthy doesn't get any easier than a shake or smoothie. By blending together a mixture of protein-rich selections, healthy fats, slow-digesting carbs, and a healthy selection of fruits and veggies, you can get an awesome meal replacement without the effort required to actually prepare a meal.

Sure, whole food choices are typically better than supplemental foods. And that's exactly why we did our best to stick with the motto of "whole food first," choosing foods rich in healthy fats (such as seeds, nuts, extra virgin olive oil, flaxseed oil), choosing lots of fruits and veggies (both fresh and frozen varieties), as well as choosing protein-rich foods like cottage cheese and yogurt.

You can use these recipes daily as a simple breakfast, a post-workout recovery drink, or a snack between meals. And with large and small serving sizes, they can be a snack or a complete meal, whichever you choose.

And remember, you're not constrained by the recipes themselves. Feel free to experiment with a variety of fruits and veggies, protein flavors, and healthy fat sources to create some of your own unique flavor combinations.

Raspberry Mocha Shake

Pw
Post-workout
Meal

5
min.
Preparation
Time

Nutritional Information

(per serving)	large	small
Calories (k/cal)	589.4	294.7
Fat (g)	18.8	9.4
Saturated (g)	3.4	1.7
Monounsaturated (g)	8.0	4.0
Polyunsaturated (g)	4.6	2.3
omega-3 (g)	0.2	0.1
omega-6 (g)	2.6	1.3
Carbohydrates (g)	40.3	20.2
fiber (g)	10.9	5.5
sugars (g)	25.0	12.5
Protein (g)	64.8	32.4

Coffee is a beverage staple across the world, and although bitter in taste on its own, it goes really well with anything sweet. In this particular shake, we've paired the bitterness of coffee with the sweetness of raspberries, adding in some chocolate to create the mocha vibe we're going for. This shake is a winner!

Instructions

Mix instant coffee and 1 tablespoon of boiling water in a countertop blender. Add ice cubes to chill the coffee. Combine the remaining ingredients. Blend on high until mixture is smooth and creamy. **Serves 1 large or 2 small.**

Hot water	1 tbsp
Instant coffee	1 tsp
Ice cubes	3
Low-fat milk	1 cup
Low-fat cottage cheese	1 cup
Raspberries (frozen)	1 cup
Chocolate whey protein (equal to 25 g protein)	1 scoop
Almonds (blanched)	2 tbsp
Fish oil	1 tsp

Variations and Options

If you are lactose intolerant or wish to avoid dairy, replace the 1 cup milk and 1 cup cottage cheese with 1 cup unsweetened soy milk (or 1 cup water and ½ scoop protein) and 1 cup plain, lactose-free yogurt. Alternatively, you can substitute with non-cow's-milk dairy (e.g. goat's milk). **If you don't like coffee or you're just looking for something different, omit the coffee and just stick with the other ingredients.** If you'd like to enhance the flavor, add a small handful of coco nibs or bitter chocolate to this shake. Coco nibs are loaded with health-promoting nutrients. **For a nutty variety, try using cashews, pine nuts or walnuts as a substitute for almonds.** **Pw** option: To create a great post-workout meal, simply **replace the milk with ½ cup of chocolate frozen yogurt.**

Mint Chocolate Shake

At

Anytime
Meal

5 min.

Preparation
Time

Nutritional Information

(per serving)	large	small
Calories (k/cal)	593.0	296.5
Fat (g)	22.4	11.2
Saturated (g)	4.7	2.4
Monounsaturated (g)	2.9	1.4
Polyunsaturated (g)	9.0	4.5
omega-3 (g)	7.3	3.6
omega-6 (g)	1.7	0.9
Carbohydrates (g)	36.9	18.4
fiber (g)	2.0	1.0
sugars (g)	27.3	13.7
Protein (g)	61.1	30.6

Unsweetened iced tea is a great no-calorie drink option that you can enjoy on its own or even in a smoothie. And iced mint tea is no exception. So instead of using artificial mint flavoring to create our Mint Chocolate Shake, we've used a soothing natural mint tea. If you like the mint-chocolate flavor combination, you'll really like this shake.

Instructions

Steep a mint tea bag in ½ cup of hot water for 5 minutes. Squeeze remaining liquid from teabag and discard. Add 1 cup of ice to the tea. Combine all ingredients in a countertop blender. Blend on high until mixture is a smooth and creamy.

Serves 1 large or 2 small.

Mint tea (strong)	½ cup
Water	½ cup
Ice	1 cup
Chocolate whey protein (equal to 50 g protein)	2 scoops
Low-fat plain yogurt	1 cup
Flaxseed oil	1 tbsp
Semi-sweet chocolate chips	1 tbsp

Variations and Options

If you are lactose intolerant or wish to avoid dairy, replace the 1 cup yogurt with 1 cup plain, lactose-free yogurt. Alternatively you can substitute with non-cow's-milk dairy (e.g. goat's milk). **If you're a coffee lover, choose ½ cup of coffee instead of the mint tea.** If you'd like to thicker up your shake, make the tea the night before and chill over night. Then add the ice, additional ingredients, and blend. **If you don't have mint tea on hand, use water and a couple of fresh mint leaves.**

Orange Chocolate Shake

Pw

Post-workout
Meal

5 min.

Preparation
Time

Nutritional Information

(per serving)	large	small
Calories (k/cal)	550.5	275.2
Fat (g)	21.0	10.5
Saturated (g)	5.7	2.9
Monounsaturated (g)	4.6	2.3
Polyunsaturated (g)	9.3	4.7
omega-3 (g)	7.3	3.6
omega-6 (g)	2.0	1.0
Carbohydrates (g)	53.9	27.0
fiber (g)	5.4	2.7
sugars (g)	43.8	21.9
Protein (g)	36.5	18.3

Chocolate and fruit are a natural culinary pairing. Oranges, raspberries and strawberries all pair well with the food of the gods. But we have a special place in our hearts for the underrated orange-chocolate combo. In case you've yet to give this combo a try, we'd love to be the first to introduce it to your kitchen. Not only does this shake taste great, it's got a great burst of natural fruit goodness too.

Instructions

Combine all ingredients in a countertop blender. Blend on high until mixture is smooth and creamy. **Serves 1 large or 2 small.**

Orange (peeled and all white stuff removed)	1
Low-fat chocolate milk	1 cup
Low-fat cottage cheese	1 cup
Flaxseed oil	1 tbsp
Ice	1 cup

Variations and Options

If you are lactose intolerant or wish to avoid dairy, replace the 1 cup chocolate milk and 1 cup cottage cheese with 1 cup chocolate soy milk (or 1 cup water and a ½ scoop chocolate protein) and 1 cup plain, lactose-free yogurt. Alternatively, you can substitute with non-cow's-milk dairy (e.g. goat's milk). **You can spice up this shake with a pinch of nutmeg or cinnamon.** If you like a thicker shake, use chocolate or coffee-flavored sugar-free yogurt in place of the milk. **For some fruit variety, feel free to experiment with other fruits such as strawberries, raspberries, or whatever other flavors strike your fancy.** **At** option: To make a great anytime shake, replace the chocolate milk with unsweetened soy milk and a scoop of chocolate whey protein.

Nutty Crunch Shake

Pw

Post-workout
Meal

5
min.

Preparation
Time

Peanut butter's strong characteristic flavor and texture always make for an awesome shake. But by adding in some raw oats for texture and chocolate protein for flavor, this shake takes it to the next level by offering that peanut butter–chocolate taste combo we've all grown to love.

Rolled-oats	3½ tbsp
Low-fat milk	1 cup
Low-fat cottage cheese	1 cup
Chocolate whey protein (equal to 25 g protein)	1 scoop
Peanut butter	2 tbsp
Ice	1 cup

Nutritional Information

(per serving)	large	small
Calories (k/cal)	634.4	317.2
Fat (g)	21.5	10.8
Saturated (g)	4.0	2.0
Monounsaturated (g)	1.2	0.6
Polyunsaturated (g)	0.6	0.3
omega-3 (g)	0.0	0.0
omega-6 (g)	0.5	0.3
Carbohydrates (g)	41.6	20.8
fiber (g)	5.0	2.5
sugars (g)	20.9	10.5
Protein (g)	68.6	34.3

Instructions

Combine all ingredients in a countertop blender. Blend on high until mixture is a smooth consistency. **Serves 1 large or 2 small.**

Variations and Options

If you are lactose intolerant or wish to avoid dairy, replace the 1 cup milk and 1 cup cottage cheese with 1 cup unsweetened soy milk (or 1 cup water and ½ cup protein powder) and 1 cup plain, lactose-free yogurt. Alternatively, you can substitute with non-cow's-milk dairy (e.g. goat's milk). **If you'd like to enhance this shake with additional flavor, replace the milk with chocolate or coffee flavored sugar-free yogurt.** For a nutty variety, substitute peanut butter with almond butter. **To spice up this shake, use a pinch of cinnamon.** **Pw** option: For a great post-workout version of this shake, add in ¼ cup of semi-sweet chocolate chips and/or substitute the peanut butter with Nutella®.

Matcha Green Tea Smoothie

At

Anytime
Meal

5 min.

Preparation
Time

Nutritional Information

(per serving)	large	small
Calories (k/cal)	566.9	283.4
Fat (g)	27.2	13.6
Saturated (g)	22.3	11.2
Monounsaturated (g)	1.4	0.7
Polyunsaturated (g)	0.3	0.2
omega-3 (g)	0.0	0.0
omega-6 (g)	0.3	0.2
Carbohydrates (g)	33.7	16.8
fiber (g)	2.5	1.3
sugars (g)	20.2	10.1
Protein (g)	46.8	23.4

It's likely no surprise that we're big proponents of green tea. This awesome beverage has health benefits too numerous to count. And the best green tea available is matcha green tea. If you have yet to try this type of tea, meet matcha – in the form of this excellent smoothie.

Instructions

Add matcha to 2 tbsp of hot water. Mix with a fork until matcha is completely dissolved. Add remaining hot water, stirring constantly. Combine all ingredients in a countertop blender. Blend on high until mixture is smooth and creamy.
Serves 1 large or 2 small.

Matcha green tea	1 tsp
Hot water	¼ cup
Banana	½
Coconut milk	½ cup
Low-fat cottage cheese	½ cup
Low-fat plain yogurt	½ cup
Vanilla whey protein (equal to 25 g protein)	1 scoop
Pure vanilla extract	1 tsp
Ice	2 cups

Variations and Options

To add a little zip to this already great smoothie, use ½ teaspoon fresh ginger (grated). **If you are lactose intolerant or wish to avoid dairy, replace the ½ cup cottage cheese and ½ cup yogurt with ½ cup unsweetened soy milk and ½ cup water or ¼ cup protein powder and ½ cup lactose-free, plain yogurt. Alternatively, you can substitute with non-cow's-milk dairy (e.g. goat's milk).**

Piña Colada Smoothie

Pw

Post-workout
Meal

5 min.

Preparation
Time

If you like Piña Coladas and getting caught in the rain... you'll probably love this excellent smoothie. Its island flavors will likely remind you of vacation time. But be careful with this one, it's so good you might be tempted to add a little rum.

Pineapple	½ cup
Banana	1
Coconut milk	½ cup
Vanilla whey protein (equal to 50 g protein)	2 scoops
Chilled green tea	1 cup
Ice	1 cup

Nutritional Information

(per serving)	large	small
Calories (k/cal)	640.0	320.0
Fat (g)	27.6	13.8
Saturated (g)	21.1	10.6
Monounsaturated (g)	1.0	0.5
Polyunsaturated (g)	0.4	0.2
omega-3 (g)	0.0	0.0
omega-6 (g)	0.3	0.1
Carbohydrates (g)	47.7	23.9
fiber (g)	6.2	3.1
sugars (g)	21.6	10.8
Protein (g)	50.2	25.1

Instructions

Combine all ingredients in a countertop blender. Blend on high until mixture is a smooth consistency. **Serves 1 large or 2 small.**

Variations and Options

Make a mango, melon, peach or strawberry colada by adding in ½ cup of any of these fruits and omitting the banana. **A tablespoon or two of grated coconut is a great addition to this smoothie as a garnish.** **Pw** option: For a refreshing post-workout treat, add ½ cup of vanilla frozen yogurt to this smoothie.

Tropical Smoothie

Pw

Post-workout
Meal

5
min.

Preparation
Time

Enjoy the tastes of the tropics with a thick, rich and healthy smoothie. It's packed with fruits, so make sure to pick seasonal varieties – they're higher in vital nutrients and they taste so much better. However, if it's the dead of winter, frozen fruits will get the job done too.

Pineapple (chilled or frozen)	½ cup
Mango (chilled or frozen)	½ cup
Peaches (chilled or frozen)	½ cup
Low-fat cottage cheese	1 cup
Low-fat milk	1 cup
Vanilla or orange flavored fish oil	1 tsp

Nutritional Information

(per serving)	large	small
Calories (k/cal)	372.3	186.2
Fat (g)	9.4	4.7
Saturated (g)	3.9	2.0
Monounsaturated (g)	2.7	1.3
Polyunsaturated (g)	2.0	1.0
omega-3 (g)	1.5	0.8
omega-6 (g)	0.4	0.2
Carbohydrates (g)	35.1	17.6
fiber (g)	1.8	0.9
sugars (g)	32.1	16.1
Protein (g)	36.9	18.4

Instructions

Combine all ingredients in a countertop blender. Blend on high until mixture is a smooth consistency. **Serves 1 large or 2 small.**

Variations and Options

If you are lactose intolerant or wish to avoid dairy, replace the 1 cup cottage cheese and 1 cup milk with 1 cup lactose-free yogurt and either 1 cup unsweetened soy milk or 1 cup water and ½ scoop protein powder. Alternatively, you can substitute with non-cow's-milk dairy (e.g. goat's milk). **Bananas, berries, nectarines, kiwi fruit, peeled apples and oranges work well as substitutes for the fruits in this smoothie.** A tablespoon or two of grated coconut is a great addition to this smoothie as a garnish.

Popeye Fruit Smoothie

Pw

Post-workout
Meal

5
min.

Preparation
Time

Nutritional Information

(per serving)	large	small
Calories (k/cal)	780.0	390.0
Fat (g)	20.0	10.0
Saturated (g)	3.7	1.9
Monounsaturated (g)	9.1	4.6
Polyunsaturated (g)	3.7	1.9
omega-3 (g)	0.2	0.1
omega-6 (g)	3.0	1.5
Carbohydrates (g)	80.0	40.0
fiber (g)	15.8	7.9
sugars (g)	36.7	18.4
Protein (g)	70.0	35.0

Spinach is a super-food high in anti-inflammatory nutrients, vitamins, minerals and alkaline potential in the body. No wonder Popeye ate it to boost his strength. As a result, we try to include spinach in many of our meals, including our shakes. And while spinach doesn't seem like it'd be a great smoothie ingredient, this shake tastes awesome as raspberries, goji berries and cashews lend their unique flavors to this drink.

Instructions

Combine all ingredients in a countertop blender. Blend on high until mixture is a smooth consistency. **Serves 1 large or 2 small.**

Raspberries (frozen)	1 cup
Spinach	1 cup
Low-fat plain yogurt	1 cup
Low-fat milk	½ cup
Cashews	¼ cup
Fruit-flavored whey protein (equal to 50 g protein)	2 scoops
Fresh goji berries	2 tbsp

Variations and Options

If you are lactose intolerant or wish to avoid dairy, replace the 1 cup yogurt and ½ cup milk with 1 cup lactose-free yogurt and either 1 cup unsweetened soy milk or 1 cup water and ½ scoop protein powder. Alternatively, you can substitute with non-cow's-milk dairy (e.g. goat's milk). **For a major vitamin boost, add up to 3 cups of spinach to the recipe.** If you can't find goji berries, you can substitute with goji berry juice or raisins. **If you don't have fruit-flavored protein powder, vanilla will work as well.**

Blueberry Madness Smoothie

At
Anytime
Meal

5 min.
Preparation
Time

Nutritional Information

(per serving)	large	small
Calories (k/cal)	656.1	328.0
Fat (g)	33.9	17.0
Saturated (g)	6.6	3.3
Monounsaturated (g)	13.2	6.6
Polyunsaturated (g)	12.2	6.1
omega-3 (g)	7.5	3.8
omega-6 (g)	4.7	2.3
Carbohydrates (g)	39.8	19.9
fiber (g)	5.2	2.6
sugars (g)	24.6	12.3
Protein (g)	47.9	23.9

Blueberries are amazing little antioxidant storehouses, full of taste and ol' fashioned healthy goodness. This shake spotlights these little berries and enhances their flavor by synergizing them with herbal tea and cashews. If you like blueberries, you'll love this shake.

Instructions

Steep a tea bag in 1 cup of hot water for 3 minutes. Add ice to chill the tea. Combine all ingredients in a countertop blender. Blend on high until mixture is smooth and creamy. **Serves 1 large or 2 small.**

Herbal fruit tea	1 cup
Water	1 cup
Ice	1½ cups
Blueberries	1 cup
Cashews	¼ cup
Low-fat cottage cheese	1½ cups
Flaxseed oil	1 tbsp
Pure vanilla extract	1 tsp
Cinnamon	1 pinch
Splenda®, to taste	

Variations and Options

If you are lactose intolerant or wish to avoid dairy, replace the 1 cup cottage cheese with 1 cup lactose-free yogurt or 1 cup unsweetened soy milk or 1 cup water and ½ scoop protein powder. Alternatively, you can substitute with non-cow's-milk dairy (e.g. goat's milk). **For some berry variety, substitute blueberries with their antioxidant-rich cousin – the blackberry.** To add some fish oil to this shake, substitute 1 teaspoon of lemon-flavored fish oil in place of flaxseed oil. **Pw** **option: For a creamier post-workout option, replace the cottage cheese with fruit-flavored yogurt.** If you'd like to avoid Splenda®, you can replace with a small amount of stevia.

V6 Supershake

Anytime
Meal

8 min.

Preparation
Time

Nutritional Information

(per serving)	large	small
Calories (k/cal)	716.1	358.1
Fat (g)	45.8	22.9
Saturated (g)	6.8	3.4
Monounsaturated (g)	30.0	15.0
Polyunsaturated (g)	6.0	3.0
omega-3 (g)	0.4	0.2
omega-6 (g)	5.6	2.8
Carbohydrates (g)	39.6	19.8
fiber (g)	9.9	5.0
sugars (g)	21.4	10.7
Protein (g)	36.5	18.3

The V6 Supershake is named after the 6 fresh veggies used in the creation of this shake. Full of wholesome veggie goodness, vitamins, minerals and phytonutrients, this shake provides a whole-food, unprocessed version of the commercial vegetable cocktail that sacrifices fiber and nutrition for mass production.

Instructions

Combine all ingredients in a countertop blender. Blend on high until mixture is smooth and creamy. **Serves 1 large or 2 small.**

Baby carrots (cooked)	¼ cup
Onion	¼ cup
Avocado	¼ cup
Tomato (small)	1
Spinach	1 cup
Cucumber (peeled)	½ cup
Low-fat cottage cheese	1 cup
Extra virgin olive oil	2 tbsp
Almonds (blanched)	2 tbsp
Lemon juice (fresh squeezed)	2 tbsp
Water	½ cup
Ice cubes	4
Dried prunes	2

Variations and Options

If you are lactose intolerant or wish to avoid dairy, replace the 1 cup cottage cheese with 1 cup lactose-free yogurt or 1 cup unsweetened soy milk or 1 cup water and ½ scoop protein powder. Alternatively, you can substitute with non-cow's-milk dairy (e.g. goat's milk). **For picky eaters, omit any vegetables you don't like and increase the volume of the ones you do like.** For some nutty variety, try using cashews, pine nuts or walruts as a substitute for almonds.

6
Meats

Because it's higher in cholesterol and saturated fat than other meats, red meat has often been shunned by the health-conscious. Yet it need not be. Leaner cuts of red meat, such as extra lean beef, venison and bison are readily available and are loaded with protein, B-vitamins and iron while being low in saturated fat. This makes lean red meat an excellent addition to your menu – as long as you're choosing leaner cuts and eating a varied diet.

But wait, there's more good news. The recipes that you'll find in this chapter make the most of every beef dish, flavoring it in a way that brings out its unique flavor and texture and/or pairing it with any number of amazing side dishes.

Please take note, though. For many of the recipes in this section, the meat takes center stage. In other words, for many of the recipes, the instructions are only provided for the meat prep. We did it this way for a good reason – so that each meat recipe could be paired with the perfect anytime or post-workout side dish. This ultimately gives you more variety and additional dining options.

And to help you along in your meal pairings, we've provided our recommendations for ideal combinations. So, all you've got to do is prepare the meat and the referenced side dish and you're set. Of course, these recommended side dishes are just suggestions. You can get creative, mixing and matching your meats and accompaniments as you like.

Speaking of meat preparation, here's an interesting tip. With meats, as with chicken and seafood, it is of the utmost importance to preheat your pans when sautéing. Preheated pans will make a sizzle when the meat first touches the pan. If you don't hear the sizzle, take the meat out quickly and wait another minute or so.

Another no-no is overloading your pan with too much meat. Too much meat will pull heat too quickly from the pan and you will be left with a pan that is not nearly as hot as it should be.

Stir-Fry Beef

At with Sautéed Spinach with Roasted Garlic (pg.194)
Pw with Roasted Garlic Barley Risotto (pg.206)

2 min.
Preparation Time

8 min.
Cooking Time

This simple stir-fry is easy to make and goes really well with any number of condiments and/or accompaniments including the Sautéed Spinach with Roasted Garlic recipe and the Roasted Garlic Barley Risotto recipe.

Sirloin steak (sliced) (170 g)	6 oz
Salt	2 pinches
Pepper	1 pinch
Olive oil spray	
Fresh garlic (minced)	1 tsp

Nutritional Information

(per serving)	large	small
Calories (k/cal)	219.5	109.7
Fat (g)	8.4	4.2
Saturated (g)	3.8	1.9
Monounsaturated (g)	3.6	1.8
Polyunsaturated (g)	0.4	0.2
omega-3 (g)	0.1	0.0
omega-6 (g)	0.3	0.2
Carbohydrates (g)	0.0	0.0
fiber (g)	0.0	0.0
sugars (g)	0.0	0.0
Protein (g)	36.0	18.0

Instructions

Season beef evenly with salt and pepper. Preheat a non-stick pan on medium heat, lightly coat with spray and add the seasoned beef. Sauté until lightly browned, stirring occasionally. Add in garlic and sauté for 1 minute more. Remove from the pan and pair with a post-workout or an anytime side dish. **Serves 1 large or 2 small.**

Variations and Options

Ground beef is a good alternative to sliced sirloin steak. **You can add sesame seeds, finely chopped shallots and cilantro for a nice finishing touch.**

The Perfect Steak

 with Sweet Balsamic Cherry Tomatoes (pg.192)

with Roasted Garlic Barley Risotto (pg.206)

2 min.
Preparation Time

10 min.
Cooking Time

Nutritional Information

(per serving)	large	small
Calories (k/cal)	263.8	131.9
Fat (g)	10.1	5.0
Saturated (g)	3.7	1.9
Monounsaturated (g)	4.1	2.0
Polyunsaturated (g)	0.4	0.2
omega-3 (g)	0.0	0.0
omega-6 (g)	0.4	0.2
Carbohydrates (g)	5.7	2.9
fiber (g)	0.0	0.0
sugars (g)	5.7	2.8
Protein (g)	37.5	18.8

Most folks love the taste of a perfectly done steak. So, with this recipe we decided to teach them how it's done. Just a few ingredients go a long way. Serve with Sweet Balsamic Cherry Tomatoes or Sautéed Garlic Barley Risotto for an amazing dinner.

Instructions

Preheat oven to 300°F with a cookie sheet and a meat rack if you have one. Preheat a non-stick frying pan on medium-high heat, lightly coat with spray and place the steak into the pan. Sear until nicely browned and then flip the steak and repeat on the other side. Place the steak into the oven and roast until desired completion (10-25 minutes). In a small bowl mix salt, pepper, cinnamon and honey (warmed). Remove steak and let it rest for 3-5 minutes on top of the stove and then serve. Pour small bowl of ingredients over steak.

Serves 1 large or 2 small.

Olive oil cooking spray	
Beef tenderloin (170 g)	6 oz
Coarse sea salt	2 pinches
Pepper	1 pinch
Ground cinnamon	1 pinch
Pure honey (warmed)	1 tsp

Variations and Options

If you are a little short on time or are impatient, you can crank the heat of your oven up to 350°F, but this will take away from the tenderness and juiciness of the final product. **Because tenderloin can be a little pricey, top sirloin steak makes a decent substitute.** If you'd like to tenderize your meat even further, marinate the steak with 2 tablespoons of pineapple juice, 1 tablespoon of soy sauce, 1 tablespoon of oil, a pinch of cinnamon and paprika. Pour marinade into a zip-lock bag and marinate steaks from 2-8 hours for optimal flavor. Remember to flip the steak to marinate both sides. Some people recommend piercing the steak with a fork during the marinating or cooking process; however, this is not necessary.

Sirloin Burger

 At with Coconut Cauliflower Mash (pg.196)
Pw with Miso Vegetable Brown Rice (pg.198)

3 min.
Preparation Time

10 min.
Cooking Time

Nutritional Information

(per serving)	large	small
Calories (k/cal)	232.9	116.4
Fat (g)	8.4	4.2
Saturated (g)	3.8	1.9
Monounsaturated (g)	3.6	1.8
Polyunsaturated (g)	0.4	0.2
omega-3 (g)	0.1	0.0
omega-6 (g)	0.3	0.2
Carbohydrates (g)	3.1	1.6
fiber (g)	0.3	0.2
sugars (g)	1.4	0.7
Protein (g)	36.2	18.1

A great-tasting burger is hard to beat. This Sirloin Burger has an excellent texture and flavor and goes great with Coconut Cauliflower Mash or Miso Vegetable Brown Rice.

Instructions

Preheat a non-stick frying pan on medium heat. Combine all ingredients except cooking spray together in a mixing bowl and stir until completely combined. Form into a round shape about ¾ inch thick. Lightly coat pan with spray and place the sirloin burger into the pan. Cook the burger until lightly browned and then gently flip and brown the other side. Cook all the way through and serve. **Serves 1 large or 2 small.**

Ground sirloin or extra lean ground beef (170 g)	6 oz
Salt	2 pinches
Pepper	1 pinch
Chili powder	1 pinch
Fresh garlic (minced)	1 tsp
Onion (finely chopped)	2 tbsp
Worcestershire sauce	1 tsp
Olive oil cooking spray	

Variations and Options

To add flavor and texture, add finely chopped peppers, corn or herbs to the burger.

Sirloin Skewers

 At with Sweet Balsamic Cherry Tomatoes (pg.192)
Pw with Chunky Tomato Spelt (pg.210)

10 min.
Preparation Time

10 min.
Cooking Time

Nutritional Information

(per serving)	large	small
Calories (k/cal)	325.6	162.8
Fat (g)	8.8	4.4
Saturated (g)	3.3	1.7
Monounsaturated (g)	3.5	1.7
Polyunsaturated (g)	0.5	0.2
omega-3 (g)	0.0	0.0
omega-6 (g)	0.3	0.2
Carbohydrates (g)	7.9	4.0
fiber (g)	1.8	0.9
sugars (g)	4.2	2.1
Protein (g)	53.7	26.9

Another great way to serve beef is on a skewer. These skewers taste great accompanied by Sweet Balsamic Cherry Tomatoes or Chunky Tomato Spelt.

Instructions

Carefully slide ingredients onto the skewer using lots of beef. (In sequence this might look like: beef-cherry tomato-beef -zucchini-beef-red onion-beef). Repeat until the beef is used up. Preheat a non-stick frying pan on medium heat, lightly coat with cooking spray and place the skewers into the pan. Sauté until lightly browned on all sides, season to taste with salt and pepper, and pair with a side. **Serves 1 large or 2 small.**

Sirloin
(1-inch cubed, 170 g) 6 oz

Cherry tomatoes   4

Zucchini   4 pieces
(cut to same size as sir oin)

Red onion   4 pieces
(large diced)

Olive oil cooking spray

Sea salt, to taste

Pepper, to taste

Variations and Options

To tenderize your meat, marinate skewers for a couple of hours or over night. Mix together ¼ cup of plain low-fat yogurt, 1 tablespoon of lemon juice, 2 teaspoons of minced garlic, ½ teaspoon of chili powder and 1 tablespoon of brown sugar.

Spaghetti Squash Spaghetti

Pw

Post-workout
Meal

15 min.
Preparation
Time

45 min.
Cooking
Time

Nutritional Information

(per serving)	large	small
Calories (k/cal)	709.1	354.6
Fat (g)	31.2	15.6
Saturated (g)	15.6	7.8
Monounsaturated (g)	10.3	5.2
Polyunsaturated (g)	2.8	1.4
omega-3 (g)	0.4	0.2
omega-6 (g)	2.2	1.1
Carbohydrates (g)	52.4	26.2
fiber (g)	9.7	4.8
sugars (g)	22.9	11.4
Protein (g)	54.7	27.3

If you love eating spaghetti but hate what it does to your stomach and hips, you're not alone. Yet spaghetti squash can act as an excellent pasta substitute. So why not simulate your favorite spaghetti recipe with this take on spaghetti with meat sauce.

Instructions

Preheat oven to 375°F. Cut squash in half and clean out the center and seeds. Place cut side up on a baking sheet and drizzle with oil or butter. Season with salt, pepper and cinnamon and then place in the oven. Bake squash for 45 minutes or until tender enough to stick a fork into it with minimal resistance. Remove from oven and allow it to cool a little. While the squash is baking, preheat a non-stick frying pan on medium heat, lightly coat with spray and add the ground sirloin. Sauté the sirloin in batches if necessary, until lightly browned and cooked all the way through. Add onions and sauté for 2 minutes more. Remove from heat, add in the tomato sauce and cashews, and set aside. Once squash has cooled a little, scoop the flesh out of the skin with a spoon, measure and add it to the meat sauce. Next, reheat in the frying pan on medium until warm. Garnish with the parmesan.

Serves 2 large or 4 small.

Spaghetti squash	4 cups
Coconut oil or butter (melted)	1 tbsp
Salt	¼ tsp
Pepper	⅛ tsp
Cinnamon	⅛ tsp
Olive oil cooking spray	
Ground sirloin or extra lean ground beef (340 g)	12 oz
Onion (small diced)	1 cup
Tomato sauce	2 cups
Cashews (crushed)	¼ cup
Parmesan cheese (grated)	½ cup

Variations and Options

Make this post-workout recipe a chicken recipe by substituting sautéed chicken breast for the ground beef. **For a lower-carb anytime dish, reduce spaghetti squash from 4 cups to 3 cups.** For a more gourmet approach, plate the warm squash first, top with the hot meat sauce and then garnish with the parmesan, adding some chopped basil on top.

Beef and Vegetable Fettuccine

At
Anytime
Meal

10 min.
Preparation Time

10 min.
Cooking Time

Nutritional Information

(per serving)	large	small
Calories (k/cal)	583.3	291.6
Fat (g)	22.6	11.3
Saturated (g)	14.2	7.1
Monounsaturated (g)	4.2	2.1
Polyunsaturated (g)	1.1	0.5
omega-3 (g)	0.1	0.1
omega-6 (g)	0.9	0.5
Carbohydrates (g)	30.5	15.3
fiber (g)	4.6	2.3
sugars (g)	12.4	6.2
Protein (g)	64.4	32.2

Once again, if you love pasta but don't eat it often due to its high-carb content, you can simulate your favorite fettuccine dish with vegetable "fettuccine". In this recipe, we use veggies cut into thin strips as a pasta substitute and cover them with a delicious meat sauce.

Instructions

Peel the outside layer of the carrots and discard. Now use the peeler and peel the carrots, zucchini and broccoli into strips and then set aside. This is the "fettuccine." With the zucchini, peel down until you reach the seeded soft center and then either mash up and add to the sauce or discard. Sauté beef (refer to instructions on page 86). Remove from pan and set aside. Preheat a small pot on medium heat and lightly coat with spray. Add the onion and sauté. Mix in coconut milk, yogurt, miso, nutmeg and pepper, bring to a simmer and stir until miso is completely dissolved. Remove from heat. Clean pan if necessary, preheat and re-spray. Add the carrot and broccoli "fettuccine" to the pan and sauté for 3 minutes. Add 2 tablespoons of broth or water and then add the zucchini and cook for 2 minutes more. Add the sauce and toss until warm. Transfer the "fettuccine" to the center of a plate, and top with the sautéed beef. **Serves 1 large or 2 small.**

"Fettuccine"

Carrot	½ cup
Zucchini	¾ cup
Broccoli stalk (imperfections trimmed)	¾ cup

Meat

Olive oil cooking spray	
Sliced sirloin or stir-fry beef (170 g)	**6 oz**

Sauce

Olive oil cooking spray	
Onion (finely diced)	¼ cup
Coconut milk	¼ cup
Yogurt	⅓ cup
Miso paste	1 tbsp
Nutmeg	1 pinch
Pepper	1 pinch
Water or vegetable broth	2 tbsp

Variations and Options

Sweet potato, yam and butternut squash are additional vegetables you can use to make the "fettuccine". For great meat substitutions, use Sautéed Chicken Breast (refer to recipe page 112) or Garlic Sautéed Prawns (refer to recipe page 150).

Texas Thin Crust Pizza

At

Anytime
Meal

10 min.
Preparation Time

10 min.
Cooking Time

Many folks have an almost instinctive love of pizza. However, on a rational level, they know it's loaded with processed carbs and saturated fats. So, when you'd rather go with your head, choose this healthy thin crust pizza.

Nutritional Information

(per serving)	large	small
Calories (k/cal)	552.1	276.1
Fat (g)	28.5	14.3
Saturated (g)	15.9	7.9
Monounsaturated (g)	9.4	4.7
Polyunsaturated (g)	1.4	0.7
omega-3 (g)	0.3	0.1
omega-6 (g)	1.0	0.5
Carbohydrates (g)	21.4	10.7
fiber (g)	2.6	1.3
sugars (g)	13.2	6.6
Protein (g)	52.5	26.3

Instructions

Preheat the oven to 400°F. Preheat a non-stick frying pan on medium heat. Lightly coat with spray, add the ground meat and season with salt and pepper. Sauté the beef until lightly browned and cooked all the way through. Add the onions, peppers and garlic and sauté for 1 minute more. Add the tomato and BBQ sauce, stir until combined and remove from heat. Lightly coat a baking sheet with spray and place the tortilla shell on the tray. Spread the beef and vegetable mixture evenly on the shell, leaving the outside half inch for the crust. Top with the pineapple and cheese and then place in the oven. Bake until cheese is melted and shell is nicely toasted (about 10 minutes). **Serves 1 large or 2 small.**

Olive oil cooking spray	
Ground sirloin or extra lean ground beef (170 g)	6 oz
Salt	¼ tsp
Pepper	⅛ tsp
Yellow onion (small diced)	¼ cup
Red pepper (small diced)	¼ cup
Garlic (minced)	2 tsp
Tomato (small diced)	¼ cup
BBQ sauce	2 tbsp
Whole wheat tortilla	1
Pineapple (tidbits or chopped)	¼ cup
Aged white cheddar (grated)	½ cup

Variations and Options

If you don't like the BBQ sauce, then substitute with tomato sauce instead. **Different cheeses will provide a range of flavors.** Substitute the garlic with roasted garlic (refer to recipe on page 194) for a gourmet flavor.

Venison Stew

Pw

Post-workout
Meal

20
min.

Preparation
Time

3
hrs.

Cooking
Time

Nutritional Information

(per serving)	large	small
Calories (k/cal)	624.8	312.4
Fat (g)	15.0	7.5
Saturated (g)	8.4	4.2
Monounsaturated (g)	3.7	1.9
Polyunsaturated (g)	1.1	0.5
omega-3 (g)	0.1	0.0
omega-6 (g)	0.7	0.3
Carbohydrates (g)	83.3	41.7
fiber (g)	13.5	6.8
sugars (g)	43.4	21.7
Protein (g)	39.2	19.6

Game meats, such as venison, are often leaner and contain a better fat profile than their corn-fed counterparts. That's why we decided to include some venison in this stew. Loaded with veggies and lean meats, this recipe is quite hearty and goes great on a cold winter day.

Instructions

Preheat a non-stick frying pan on medium heat and lightly coat with spray. Cooking in batches add the venison. Sauté until nicely browned on all sides and then remove and set aside. Repeat until all meat is browned. Preheat a large pot on medium-high heat. Add the butter and then the onions, carrots, parsnips and garlic. Sauté until veggies begin to brown. Add in the tomatoes and sauté for 5 minutes more. Add the salt, pepper, thyme, honey, balsamic vinegar and broth as well as the browned venison to the pot. Bring to a boil and then immediately reduce heat to low and cover with a tight-fitting lid. Simmer on low for 3 hours. If you boil the stew for more than a few seconds, the meat will become tough. Simmering is very important. You can check if the meat is tender enough by removing one piece, placing it on your cutting board and cutting with your fork. If your fork goes through the meat with little resistance, it is ready. If not, continue simmering on low until it is "fork tender." **Serves 2 large or 4 small.**

Olive oil cooking spray	
Venison stew meat (deer meat, 1-inch cubed, 680 g)	1 lb 8 oz
Butter	2 tbsp
Onion (large dice)	2 cups
Baby carrots (halved)	2 cups
Parsnips (peeled, 1-inch cubed)	2 cups
Garlic cloves (peeled, halved)	8
Tomato (rough chopped)	2 cups
Salt	½ tsp
Pepper	½ tsp
Dried thyme	½ tsp
Honey	2 tbsp
Balsamic vinegar	2 tbsp
Beef broth	3 cups

Variations and Options

For a hearty beef stew, replace venison with beef.

Lamb Chili

Pw
Post-workout
Meal

20
min.
Preparation
Time

3
hrs.
Cooking
Time

Nutritional Information

(per serving)	large	small
Calories (k/cal)	585.7	292.8
Fat (g)	11.3	5.7
Saturated (g)	5.9	3.0
Monounsaturated (g)	2.5	1.3
Polyunsaturated (g)	1.4	0.7
omega-3 (g)	0.3	0.2
omega-6 (g)	0.9	0.5
Carbohydrates (g)	82.7	41.4
fiber (g)	22.5	11.3
sugars (g)	16.4	8.2
Protein (g)	38.2	19.1

Lamb is a great alternative to beef. Although it's typically recorded with a higher fat content than lean beef, most of the lamb's fat is on the edges of the meat – there's very little marbling. As a result, much of this fat can be discarded. In this recipe, lamb is used along with a host of veggies, beans and spices, to create a chili quite unlike any you've tasted before.

Instructions

Preheat a non-stick frying pan on medium heat and lightly coat with spray. Cooking in batches, add the lamb. Sauté until nicely browned on all sides. Remove and set aside. Repeat until all meat is browned. Preheat a large pot on medium-high heat. Add the oil or butter and then the onions and peppers. Sauté until peppers begin to brown. Add the garlic and sauté for 1 minute more. Add the cumin, chili powder and tomato. Add in the chicken broth, honey, worcestershire and the cooked lamb. Bring to a boil and then immediately reduce heat to low and cover with a tight-fitting lid. Simmer on low for 2 hours and then add in the black beans and kidney beans and simmer for another hour. If you boil the stew for any more than a few seconds, the meat will become tough. Simmering is very important. You can check if the meat is tender enough by removing one piece, placing it on your cutting board and cutting it with your fork. If your fork goes through the meat with little resistance, it is ready. If not, continue simmering on low until it is "fork tender." **Serves 3 large or 6 small.**

Olive oil cooking spray	
Lamb stew meat (1-inch cubed, 680 g)	1 lb 8 oz
Coconut oil or butter	1 tbsp
Onion (large diced)	1 cup
Red bell pepper (large diced)	1 cup
Garlic (minced)	2 tbsp
Cumin	1 tsp
Chili powder	1 tbsp
14 oz cans whole peeled tomato (crushed with your hands)	2
Chicken broth	2 cups
Honey	2 tbsp
Worcestershire sauce	1 tbsp
Black beans (cooked or canned, drained, 1 can)	1½ cups
Red kidney beans (cooked or canned, drained, 1 can)	1½ cups

Variations and Options

If you want to spice this chili recipe up, add in ¼ cup chopped jalepeño peppers with the garlic. **You can bring some life to the color of this recipe by adding 2 cups frozen corn at the last minute and then garnishing a serving with finely chopped green onion.**

Beefy Mushroom Onion Broth

At

Anytime
Meal

10 min.
Preparation
Time

20 min.
Cooking
Time

Nutritional Information

(per serving)	large	small
Calories (k/cal)	513.0	256.5
Fat (g)	27.0	13.5
Saturated (g)	8.3	4.1
Monounsaturated (g)	11.3	5.6
Polyunsaturated (g)	5.3	2.6
omega-3 (g)	0.2	0.1
omega-6 (g)	4.8	2.4
Carbohydrates (g)	18.8	9.4
fiber (g)	6.0	3.0
sugars (g)	3.8	1.9
Protein (g)	48.8	24.4

Most folks wouldn't consider soup an entire meal, but many of the GN soup recipes make excellent meals on their own. Take this recipe, as an example. Loaded with veggies and meat, it's as hearty as you can get while still eating with a spoon. And take special note of the textures. Bean sprouts and sesame seeds add a nice crunch to this meal.

Instructions

Soup Base Preheat a large pot on medium-high heat. Add oil, onions and cabbage and sauté until lightly browned, stirring frequently. Remove from pot and set aside. Now add mushrooms, pepper, thyme, garlic and 2 tablespoons of the beef broth. Sauté until the mushrooms are cooked, stirring frequently. Add the cooked onions, cabbage, worcestershire sauce, and broth into the pot and remove from heat.

Soup Garnish Season the beef with salt and chili powder. Preheat a large non-stick frying pan on medium heat. Lightly coat with spray and sauté beef until nicely browned. Sauté in smaller batches and re-spray the pan if needed. Add the sautéed beef, sprouts and sesame seeds to the soup. Reheat the soup and enjoy. To maintain the tenderness of the meat, avoid bringing the soup to a boil after the meat has been added. **Serves 4 large or 8 small.**

Soup Base

Coconut oil or butter	1 tbsp
Yellow onion (sliced)	1 cup
Napa cabbage or bok choy (sliced)	2 cups
Button mushrooms (sliced)	4 cups
Pepper	½ tsp
Dried thyme	1 tsp
Garlic (minced)	2 tbsp
Beef broth	6 cups
Worcestershire sauce	1 tbsp

Soup Garnish

Sirloin steak (sliced, 740 g)	1 lb 10 oz
Salt	1 tsp
Chili powder	1 tsp
Olive oil cooking spray	
Bean sprouts	2 cups
Sesame seeds	½ cup

Variations and Options

For a great post-workout meal, make a classic beef and barley soup by adding 2 cups of cooked barley. **Green or purple cabbage also goes well in this soup in place of the napa cabbage.**

Tomato Basil Soup
with Sirloin Meatballs

At	Pw	15 min.	25 min.
Anytime Meal	Post-workout Meal	Preparation Time	Cooking Time

Nutritional Information

(per serving)	large	small
Calories (k/cal)	418.5	209.3
Fat (g)	16.5	8.3
Saturated (g)	9.0	4.5
Monounsaturated (g)	4.5	2.3
Polyunsaturated (g)	0.8	0.4
omega-3 (g)	0.1	0.0
omega-6 (g)	0.7	0.3
Carbohydrates (g)	28.5	14.3
fiber (g)	5.3	2.6
sugars (g)	18.0	9.0
Protein (g)	39.0	19.5

When most people think tomato soup, they probably think of a salty, watered-down canned version they ate once and never ate again. But don't make the mistake of thinking that this recipe is anything like that. Full of veggie goodness as well as sirloin meatballs, this soup eats like a meal.

Instructions

Soup Garnish Season the beef with salt and pepper and form into 1½ inch balls. Preheat a large non-stick frying pan on medium heat and add 1 tablespoon oil. Sauté the meatballs in batches until browned and then set aside. Spray pan with oil if needed between batches.

Soup Base Preheat a large pot on medium-high heat. Add oil and onions, and sauté until lightly browned, stirring frequently. Add garlic, cumin, fennel, paprika, 2 tablespoons of broth, and sauté for one minute more, stirring constantly. Add the tomatoes and bring to a boil. Reduce heat and simmer for 5 minutes, stirring occasionally. Now add the remaining broth, balsamic vinegar, honey and meatballs and simmer for 15 minutes, continue stirring occasionally. Add the salt, pepper and basil and remove from heat. The soup is ready to enjoy. **Serves 4 large or 8 small.**

Soup Garnish

Ground sirloin (650 g)	**1 lb 7 oz**
Salt	**1 tsp**
Pepper	**½ tsp**
Olive oil cooking spray	
Coconut oil or butter	**1 tbsp**

Soup Base

Coconut oil or butter	**2 tbsp**
Yellow onion (small dice)	**1½ cups**
Garlic (minced)	**2 tbsp**
Cumin (ground)	**1 tsp**
Fennel seed (ground)	**1 tsp**
Paprika	**1 tsp**
Vegetable broth	**2 cups**
Tomatoes (chopped)	**7 cups**
Balsamic vinegar	**2 tbsp**
Honey	**2 tbsp**
Salt	**1 tsp**
Pepper	**½ tsp**
Fresh basil (thin sliced)	**¼ cup**

Variations and Options

For a delicious salad dressing, omit the soup garnish and use 2 parts soup base, 1 part olive oil and 1 part balsamic vinegar. **For a tasty tomato sauce, omit the vegetable broth.** For some meat variety, substitute the meatballs with chicken or prawns. **For a smoother option, purée in a blender before adding the meatballs.** If you're feeling cheesy, garnish with freshly grated parmesan cheese. **For a lower-carb anytime meal, reduce honey to 1 tablespoon.** For a higher-carb post-workout meal, serve with whole grain garlic toast.

Mediterranean Salad with Beef

At
Anytime
Meal

5 min.
Preparation
Time

5 min.
Cooking
Time

The hallmark of a good Mediterranean salad is the excellent combo of cucumber, tomatoes and olives and/or olive oil. With our beefy Mediterranean salad we added some additional ingredients that you're sure to love.

Nutritional Information

(per serving)	large	small
Calories (k/cal)	518.4	259.2
Fat (g)	23.1	11.6
Saturated (g)	12.9	6.4
Monounsaturated (g)	8.0	4.0
Polyunsaturated (g)	1.4	0.7
omega-3 (g)	0.3	0.1
omega-6 (g)	0.9	0.4
Carbohydrates (g)	20.9	10.5
fiber (g)	4.3	2.2
sugars (g)	10.9	5.4
Protein (g)	56.6	28.3

Instructions

Combine all the ingredients in a large mixing bowl. Drizzle one serving of your favorite dressing on the salad and serve. **Serves 1 large or 2 small.**

Dressing

Greek Vinaigrette
(recipe on pg.246)

Salad

Stir-fry beef (recipe on pg.86, 170 g)	5 oz
Small olives (sliced)	5
Cucumber (large diced)	1 cup
Tomato (large diced)	1 cup
Low-fat feta cheese (crumbled)	½ cup
Onion (thin sliced)	½ cup

Variations and Options

Serve with 2 tablespoons of Greek Vinaigrette. **For a great post-workout meal, add ½ cup of chickpeas or beans to this salad and serve with whole grain bread.** For some veggie variety, substitute onion with grated fennel or red pepper. Also, you can substitute fresh tomato with sundried tomato.

7
Poultry

Chicken is one of the most commonly consumed meats among the health conscious. It likely owes this popularity to the fact that it's relatively cheap, lean, and very versatile. Chicken complements almost every grain, vegetable, spice and fruit. And if prepared in bulk once a week, it can be portioned out and reheated when it's time to eat.

The recipes that you'll find in this chapter make the most of every chicken dish, flavoring it in a way that brings out its unique flavor and texture and/or pairing it with any number of amazing side dishes.

As with the meat section, keep in mind that for many of the chicken recipes, the chicken takes center stage. In other words, for many of the recipes, the instructions are only provided for the chicken prep. We did it this way for a good reason – so that each chicken recipe could be paired with the perfect anytime or post-workout side dish. This ultimately gives you more variety and additional dining options.

And to help you along in your meal pairings, we've provided our recommendations for ideal combinations. So, all you've got to do is prepare the chicken and the referenced side dish and you're set. Of course, these recommended side dishes are just suggestions. You can get creative, mixing and matching your poultry and accompaniments as you like.

Sautéed Chicken Breast

 with Sautéed Spinach with Roasted Garlic (pg.194)
Pw with Vegetable Lentil Pâté (pg.214)

2 min.
Preparation Time

8 min.
Cooking Time

Nutritional Information

(per serving)	large	small
Calories (k/cal)	176.0	88.0
Fat (g)	2.1	1.1
Saturated (g)	0.6	0.3
Monounsaturated (g)	0.5	0.3
Polyunsaturated (g)	0.1	0.1
omega-3 (g)	0.4	0.2
omega-6 (g)	0.3	0.2
Carbohydrates (g)	0.0	0.0
fiber (g)	0.0	0.0
sugars (g)	0.0	0.0
Protein (g)	39.3	19.6

Lean chicken breasts provide a great helping of protein with minimal fat. In addition, chicken breasts are very versatile and can be combined with most of the GN condiments, soups or sides. To start with, try pairing with Sautéed Spinach with Roasted Garlic (anytime) or Vegetable Lentil Pâté (post-workout).

Instructions

Season chicken evenly with salt, pepper and paprika. Preheat a non-stick pan on medium heat, lightly coat with spray and add the seasoned chicken. Sauté until lightly browned all over and cooked all the way through, stirring occasionally. Remove from the pan and pair with a post-workout or an anytime option. **Serves 1 large or 2 small.**

Boneless skinless chicken breast (cut into ½ inch strips, 170 g)	**6 oz**
Salt	**2 pinches**
Pepper	**1 pinch**
Paprika	**1 pinch**
Olive oil cooking spray	

Variations and Options

For some spice variety, try using different spices on the chicken such as fennel and cumin. Another nice touch could be to use ½ tablespoon of miso paste or curry powder with a touch of veggie broth. **Try using either condiments or puréed soup as a sauce for the chicken.** For an amazing flavor boost, add finely diced onions and minced garlic to the chicken after it is cooked and then sauté for 2 minutes more.

Baked Chicken Strips

 Portobello Pizzas (pg.184)
 with Roasted Garlic Barley Risotto (pg.206)

5 min.
Preparation Time

15 min.
Cooking Time

Nutritional Information

(per serving)	large	small
Calories (k/cal)	408.7	204.3
Fat (g)	14.7	7.4
Saturated (g)	8.3	4.2
Monounsaturated (g)	3.1	1.5
Polyunsaturated (g)	2.2	1.1
omega-3 (g)	0.9	0.4
omega-6 (g)	0.9	0.5
Carbohydrates (g)	22.5	11.2
fiber (g)	3.0	1.5
sugars (g)	2.9	1.5
Protein (g)	46.5	23.3

Breaded chicken breasts are a bar or pub favorite usually high in processed carbs and hydrogenated fats. In this recipe, we lightly bread the chicken with whole grain crumbs and coconut for a nutritious and tasty coating. We recommend serving these chicken strips with Portobello Pizzas (anytime) or Roasted Garlic Barley Risotto (post-workout).

Instructions

Preheat the oven to 350°F. Season chicken evenly with salt, pepper and paprika. Add the egg and water to a mixing bowl, whisk together well and set aside. Mix the breadcrumbs and coconut together in a separate mixing bowl and set aside. Dip the chicken in the egg and toss until coated completely. Remove and allow excess to drip off for 1 or 2 seconds and then place directly into the breadcrumbs/coconut mixture. Roll until nicely coated. Lightly coat a cookie sheet with spray and place the strips onto the tray and then into the oven. Bake until golden brown or cooked through (about 15 minutes). You can remove the largest strip and cut it in half to check doneness.

Serves 1 large or 2 small.

Boneless skinless chicken breast (cut into ½ inch strips 170 g)	6 oz
Salt	2 pinches
Pepper	1 pinch
Paprika	1 pinch
Omega-3 egg	1
Water	2 tbsp
Coarse whole wheat breadcrumbs	¼ cup
Grated coconut	¼ cup
Olive oil cooking spray	

Variations and Options

For some spice variety, try using different spices on the chicken such as fennel and cumin, or curry powder. Garnish with some fresh chopped parsley or cilantro for a finishing touch. **To make teriyaki sesame chicken strips combine a tablespoon of soy sauce and melted honey to the egg and substitute sesame seeds for coconut. Then follow the rest of the instructions as they appear.**

Fruity Chicken Skewers

At with Stuffed Zucchini (pg.186)
Pw with Fruity Cashew Quinoa (pg.208)

10 min.
Preparation Time

15 min.
Cooking Time

Fruits usually pair well with chicken and in this recipe we've given you a great way to sweeten up your chicken breasts. This combination of chicken, fruits and sweet veggies goes especially well with flavorful dishes like our Stuffed Zucchini (anytime) and our Fruity Cashew Quinoa (post-workout).

Nutritional Information

(per serving)	large	small
Calories (k/cal)	369.0	184.5
Fat (g)	14.0	7.0
Saturated (g)	7.9	4.0
Monounsaturated (g)	3.5	1.8
Polyunsaturated (g)	0.6	0.3
omega-3 (g)	0.4	0.2
omega-6 (g)	0.5	0.3
Carbohydrates (g)	20.1	10.1
fiber (g)	2.7	1.4
sugars (g)	12.9	6.5
Protein (g)	40.7	20.4

Instructions

Preheat oven to 350°F. Carefully slide ingredients onto the skewer using lots of chicken. (For example, chicken-pineapple-chicken-apple-chicken-red pepper-chicken-onion-chicken). Continue making skewers until the chicken is used up. Combine melted butter, ginger, salt and chili powder in a small bowl. Place the skewers on a baking tray or in a casserole dish and then brush with the butter mixture on all sides. Place skewers in the oven and bake until chicken is cooked through (12-15 minutes). You can check the doneness of the chicken by tearing a piece in half. Serve and enjoy! **Serves 1 large or 2 small.**

Bamboo skewer sticks	
Boneless skinless chicken breast (1-inch cubed, 170 g)	6 oz
Pineapple (1-inch cubed)	3 pieces
Apple (core removed, 1-inch cubed)	3 pieces
Red pepper (cut into large pieces)	3 pieces
Onion (cut into large pieces)	3 pieces
Butter (melted)	1 tbsp
Ginger	½ tsp
Salt	¼ tsp
Chili powder	¼ tsp

Variations and Options

For a lower-calorie meal, substitute fruit with vegetables. Zucchini and garlic are great options. **For a more tenderized and flavorful meat, marinate the skewers for a couple of hours (or over night) in a mixture of 2 tablespoons oil, 3 tablespoons acidic juice (lemon, lime or orange), ½ teaspoon ginger and salt and pepper to taste.**

Roast Chicken Breast

 with Sweet Balsamic Cherry Tomatoes (pg.192)

with Chickpea Cakes (pg.212)

2 min.
Preparation Time

30 min.
Cooking Time

If you're looking for a slower-cooked, juicier chicken meal, this roast chicken breast will fit the bill. Serving alongside juicy and sweet cherry tomatoes (anytime) or chickpea cakes (post-workout) is sure to make this recipe a hit. And don't forget, this meal also goes great with one of our homemade condiments.

Boneless skinless chicken breast (170 g) — 6 oz

Olive oil cooking spray

Salt	2 pinches
Pepper	1 pinch
Coriander	1 pinch
Cumin	1 pinch

Nutritional Information

(per serving)	large	small
Calories (k/cal)	176.0	88.0
Fat (g)	2.1	1.1
Saturated (g)	0.6	0.3
Monounsaturated (g)	0.5	0.3
Polyunsaturated (g)	0.1	0.1
omega-3 (g)	0.4	0.2
omega-6 (g)	0.3	0.2
Carbohydrates (g)	0.0	0.0
fiber (g)	0.0	0.0
sugars (g)	0.0	0.0
Protein (g)	39.3	19.6

Instructions

Preheat oven to 300°F. Give the chicken breast a light spray and then sprinkle desired amount of spices on both sides. Place the chicken on a baking tray or casserole dish and bake until cooked through (20-30 minutes depending on size). Remove from the oven, check for doneness, serve and enjoy.

Serves 1 large or 2 small.

Variations and Options

If you like your chicken breast with a nicely browned exterior, you can sauté the seasoned breast in a preheated non-stick frying pan until golden brown and then carry out step 3 and 4. **You can use any of the GN condiments as a garnish for your chicken breast. This not only adds to the appearance, but heightens the flavor.**

Salisturkey Steaks

At with Coconut Cauliflower Mash (pg.196)
Pw with Miso Vegetable Brown Rice (pg.198)

3 min.
Preparation Time

10 min.
Cooking Time

Nutritional Information

(per serving)	large	small
Calories (k/cal)	345.9	172.9
Fat (g)	15.5	7.7
Saturated (g)	4.0	2.0
Monounsaturated (g)	5.5	2.7
Polyunsaturated (g)	3.6	1.8
omega-3 (g)	0.2	0.1
omega-6 (g)	3.3	1.6
Carbohydrates (g)	16.5	8.3
fiber (g)	1.6	0.8
sugars (g)	7.8	3.9
Protein (g)	35.1	17.6

You might be familiar with the famous Salisbury steak, a minced piece of beef shaped to resemble a steak and served in a brown sauce. Well, as the traditional Salisbury steak contains more fat and gravy than we'd like, we've created a Salisturkey steak. Served alongside our Coconut Cauliflower Mash (anytime) or Miso Vegetable Brown Rice (post-workout), this might just become your favorite dish.

Instructions

Preheat a non-stick frying pan on medium heat. Combine all ingredients, except spray, together in a mixing bowl and stir until completely combined. Form into an oval shape about ¾ inch thick. Lightly coat pan with spray and place the turkey steak into the pan. Cook until lightly browned and then gently flip and brown the other side. Cook all the way through and serve. **Serves 2 large or 4 small.**

Ground turkey (170 g)	**6 oz**
Egg white	**1**
Large flake oats	**2 tbsp**
Sweet onion (fine dice)	**¼ cup**
Pure honey	**1 tsp**
Salt	**1 pinch**
Cumin	**1 pinch**
Chili powder	**1 pinch**
Olive oil cooking spray	

Variations and Options

Keep in mind that you can make big batches of these steaks and freeze them. Just pull the number of steaks you need out of the freezer the night before and defrost in the fridge over night.

Ground Turkey Casserole

At

Anytime
Meal

10 min.
Preparation
Time

30 min.
Cooking
Time

Nutritional Information

(per serving)	large	small
Calories (k/cal)	630.7	315.4
Fat (g)	29.9	14.9
Saturated (g)	7.4	3.7
Monounsaturated (g)	13.8	6.9
Polyunsaturated (g)	6.3	3.1
omega-3 (g)	0.2	0.1
omega-6 (g)	5.8	2.9
Carbohydrates (g)	36.0	18.0
fiber (g)	10.0	5.0
sugars (g)	15.1	7.6
Protein (g)	54.5	27.2

Casseroles might remind you of Mom's home cooking. And whether that's a good thing or a bad thing, remember this. Our Ground Turkey Casserole is a veggie and protein packed crowd pleaser that's both easy to make and hearty to eat.

Instructions

Preheat oven to 350°F. Add the navy beans, half the milk, turmeric, coriander and salt to a blender and purée until smooth. Set aside and stir in the rest of the milk and the vegetable broth. Preheat a non-stick frying pan on medium heat and lightly coat with spray. Sauté the turkey in batches until lightly browned, then transfer to a large casserole dish. Add remaining ingredients to the casserole dish, including the puréed bean mixture, and cover. Stir well to incorporate and bake for 25-30 minutes. **Serves 3 large or 6 small.**

Navy beans (cooked or canned, drained)	½ cup
Milk	1 cup
Turmeric	1 tsp
Coriander	1 tsp
Salt	1 tsp
Vegetable broth	1 cup
Olive oil cooking spray	
Ground turkey (600 g)	1 lb 5 oz
Sweet onion (large dice)	1 cup
Baby carrots (thin sliced)	1½ cups
Asparagus (cut into 1-inch pieces)	1½ cups
Green cabbage (grated)	2 cups
Almonds (sliced)	½ cup
Low-fat aged white cheddar (shredded)	1½ cups

Variations and Options

For some veggie variety, experiment with different vegetables, such as cauliflower, broccoli, zucchini, corn and peas. **For some cheesy variety, use havarti, swiss or parmesan cheeses in place of cheddar.**

Classy Chicken

At
Anytime Meal

15 min.
Preparation Time

25 min.
Cooking Time

Nutritional Information

(per serving)	large	small
Calories (k/cal)	470.9	235.5
Fat (g)	18.5	9.3
Saturated (g)	13.7	6.9
Monounsaturated (g)	2.2	1.1
Polyunsaturated (g)	0.8	0.4
omega-3 (g)	0.1	0.0
omega-6 (g)	0.6	0.3
Carbohydrates (g)	19.4	9.7
fiber (g)	3.5	1.8
sugars (g)	10.2	5.1
Protein (g)	56.6	28.3

This is chicken dressed up to the nines. With a bounty of unique flavor combinations including miso, coconut, curry and peaches, this chicken dish looks amazing and tastes even better. Whether eaten alone or with company, you'll love this classy dish.

Instructions

Preheat the oven to 400°F. Whisk miso and coconut milk together until miso is completely dissolved. Preheat a non-stick frying pan on medium heat and lightly coat with spray. Add the chicken (in batches if necessary) and sauté until lightly browned on both sides. Transfer to a large casserole dish. Return pan to medium heat and re-spray pan if needed. Add the red pepper, onion, garlic, curry powder and cumin, and sauté for 1 minute. Add miso mixture, peach, broccoli, asparagus and sautéed vegetables to casserole dish. Evenly top with grated cheese. Place in the oven and bake for 25 minutes or until the cheese is lightly browned.

Serves 3 large or 6 small.

Shiro miso paste	1 tbsp
Coconut milk	¾ cup
Olive oil cooking spray	
Boneless skinless chicken breast (1-inch cubed, 510 g)	1 lb 2 oz
Red pepper (large diced)	1 cup
Onion (large diced)	1 cup
Garlic (minced)	1 tbsp
Curry powder	1 tbsp
Cumin	½ tsp
Peach (small diced)	1 cup
Broccoli florets (small)	1 cup
Asparagus (cut into 1-inch pieces)	1 cup
Aged white cheddar (grated)	1½ cups

Variations and Options

For some veggie variety, replace those above with your favorites or whatever is fresh and local. **If you don't like curry flavor you can omit the curry powder and season with coriander and paprika instead.**

Pesto Chicken Pizza

Pw

Post-workout
Meal

10 min.
Preparation
Time

10 min.
Cooking
Time

Nutritional Information

(per serving)	large	small
Calories (k/cal)	658.4	329.2
Fat (g)	20.8	10.4
Saturated (g)	4.9	2.4
Monounsaturated (g)	11.1	5.5
Polyunsaturated (g)	1.2	0.6
omega-3 (g)	0.7	0.3
omega-6 (g)	1.1	0.6
Carbohydrates (g)	50.9	25.5
fiber (g)	15.9	8.0
sugars (g)	7.4	3.7
Protein (g)	67.0	33.5

Pizza seems to have an almost primal draw, with people in all cultures eating some form of the dish. Of course, regardless of its widespread appeal, pizza has never been known as a "healthy" offering, because of the fact that it's typically high in processed carbs and saturated fats. With this dish, we've lightened it up by using our own homemade pesto, chicken, and a host of veggies – all on a whole wheat tortilla. If you like pizza, you'll certainly come back for seconds of this thin-crusted alternative.

Instructions

Season chicken with salt and pepper and then follow the cooking instructions for Sautéed Chicken Breast (refer to instructions on page 112). Set aside. Preheat oven at 400°F. Lightly coat a baking sheet with spray and place the tortilla shell on the tray. Spread the pesto base evenly around the shell leaving the outside inch free for the crust. Combine all the other ingredients except for the cheese in a mixing bowl and toss until mixed together. Spread evenly covering the pesto. Top with the cheese and bake until cheese is melted and shell is lightly toasted (about 10 minutes). **Serves 1 large or 2 small.**

Boneless skinless Chicken breast (170 g)	6 oz
Salt	¼ tsp
Pepper	⅛ tsp
Olive oil cooking spray	
Whole wheat tortilla	
Pesto	3 tbsp
Broccoli florets (small)	¼ cup
Sundried tomato (thin sliced)	¼ cup
Asparagus (cut into ½ inch pieces)	½ cup
Aged white Cheddar	½ cup

Variations and Options

For a flavor variety, try using Yummy Hummus (pg.262), Sundried Tomato Tzatziki (pg.258) or Rosemary Eggplant (pg.250) as a substitute for the pesto. **Use seasonal vegetables whenever possible as they not only taste better but have a healthier nutritional profile.** For a cheesy variety, try using mozzarella, feta, havarti or swiss instead of cheddar.

8-Layer Dinner

Pw
Post-workout Meal

10 min. — Preparation Time

25 min. — Cooking Time

Nutritional Information

(per serving)	large	small
Calories (k/cal)	666.6	333.3
Fat (g)	15.4	7.7
Saturated (g)	1.7	0.8
Monounsaturated (g)	8.4	4.2
Polyunsaturated (g)	3.8	1.9
omega-3 (g)	0.1	0.1
omega-6 (g)	3.3	1.7
Carbohydrates (g)	74.8	37.4
fiber (g)	19.9	9.9
sugars (g)	17.0	8.5
Protein (g)	57.3	28.6

If you like being able to chuck a bunch of ingredients together and bake them into a simple and delicious dinner, you'll appreciate this 8-layered dish. Full of great and complementary flavors, this dish brings a Mexican flavor to your dinner table.

Instructions

Preheat the oven to 350°F. Season chicken with salt and pepper. Preheat a non-stick frying pan on medium heat and lightly coat with spray. Add the chicken (in batches if necessary) and sauté until lightly browned on all sides. Remove and set aside. Clean the pan if necessary and preheat again on medium. Add the sweet potatoes and the salsa and sauté for 5 minutes. Now layer the ingredients in a large, shallow casserole dish starting with the chicken, and then the sweet potato/salsa, black beans, onion, corn, peas and almonds. Bake for 25 minutes and then serve.
Serves 3 large or 6 small.

Boneless skinless chicken breast (1-inch cubed, 510 g)	1 lb 2 oz
Salt	½ tsp
Pepper	¼ tsp
Olive oil cooking spray	
Sweet potato (peeled, thin sliced)	2 cups
Salsa	1 cup
Black beans (cooked or canned, drained, 1 can)	1½ cups
Onion (small dice)	1 cup
Corn (canned or frozen)	1 cup
Peas (canned or frozen)	1 cup
Almonds (sliced)	½ cup

Variations and Options

You can substitute the vegetables in this dish with your favorites or whatever is in season. **If you have a large skillet or wok, you can sauté ingredients instead of baking in the oven. Simply cook chicken throughout and then remove from pan. Next, add the sweet potato and salsa and thoroughly cook. Finally, add the remaining ingredients including chicken, and sauté until hot.** You can substitute the salsa with any of the puréed soup bases for a completely different meal.

Mexican Chicken Souvlaki

Pw

Post-workout
Meal

10 min.
Preparation
Time

5 min.
Cooking
Time

Nutritional Information

(per serving)	large	small
Calories (k/cal)	592.9	296.5
Fat (g)	15.9	8.0
Saturated (g)	1.9	0.9
Monounsaturated (g)	7.4	3.7
Polyunsaturated (g)	2.9	1.5
omega-3 (g)	0.6	0.3
omega-6 (g)	1.7	0.9
Carbohydrates (g)	52.5	26.3
fiber (g)	10.4	5.2
sugars (g)	7.1	3.5
Protein (g)	59.9	30.0

Inspired by Mexican and Greek cuisine, these two cultures collide in this Mexican Chicken Souvlaki. The combination of fresh veggies, avocados and sundried tomato tzatziki creates a fresh and delicious meal that can be served alone or wrapped up in whole wheat tortillas.

Instructions

Sauté chicken (refer to instructions on page 112). Set aside. Combine all ingredients (including Tzatziki; page 258) in a mixing bowl. Place approximately 1½ cups of the mixture across the bottom half of each tortilla. Fold the bottom about ¼ of the way up. Fold over each of the ends and then roll tightly from the bottom to the top. Serve and enjoy or take to go. If you can't fit all the ingredients in the tortillas, then serve the remaining mixture as a side salad. **Serves 1 large or 2 small.**

Boneless skinless chicken breast (170 g)	6 oz
Tomato (sliced)	½ cup
Avocado (small cubed)	¼ cup
Sweet onion (sliced)	¼ cup
Yellow pepper (sliced)	¼ cup
Cucumber (thin sliced)	¼ cup
Low-fat cottage cheese	⅔ cup
Sundried Tomato Tzatziki	¼ cup
Whole wheat tortillas	2

Variations and Options

You can substitute the chicken with Stir-fry Beef (pg.86) or Garlic Sautéed Prawns (pg.150) for a new flavor and texture. **For some veggie variety, substitute the veggies above with roasted squash, sweet onion and tomato.**

Caramelized Beet and Fennel Soup with Chicken

At **Pw** **10** min. **50** min.

Anytime Meal   Post-workout Meal   Preparation Time   Cooking Time

Nutritional Information

(per serving)	large	small
Calories (k/cal)	426.8	213.4
Fat (g)	15.8	7.9
Saturated (g)	4.5	2.3
Monounsaturated (g)	6.8	3.4
Polyunsaturated (g)	3.0	1.5
omega-3 (g)	0.1	0.0
omega-6 (g)	2.7	1.3
Carbohydrates (g)	29.3	14.6
fiber (g)	7.5	3.8
sugars (g)	18.8	9.4
Protein (g)	42.0	21.0

If you've got a sweet tooth, you'll love the sweetness that our purple friend, the beet, lends to this soup. Beets are quite nutrient-rich and are high in betaine, a nutrient that can help reduce heart disease risk by lowering homocysteine levels in the body. So enjoy this sweet soup post-workout, knowing that you just got a double dose of heart disease protection – exercise + beet betaine.

Instructions

Soup Base Preheat a large pot on medium-high heat. Add oil, beets, fennel root, honey, fennel seed, cinnamon and chili powder. Sauté until the juices have thickened. Add water, chicken broth and salt. Cover, reduce heat to medium-low and simmer until the beets are soft (approximately 45 minutes). Let mixture cool for a few minutes. Purée with a blender or food processor until smooth and then pour back into the pot. Remove from heat.

Soup Garnish Season chicken with salt. Preheat a large non-stick frying pan on medium heat and lightly coat with spray. Sauté chicken (in batches if necessary) until lightly browned and completely cooked (re-spraying if needed between batches). Add to soup base. Add the chicken and almonds to the soup base, reheat on medium and serve. To maintain the tenderness of the meat, avoid bringing the soup to a boil after the chicken has been added. **Serves 4 large or 8 small.**

Soup Base

Coconut oil or butter	1 tbsp
Beets (peeled, rough chopped)	4 cups
Fennel root (core removed, rough chopped)	1 cup
Pure honey	2 tbsp
Fennel seed (ground)	1 tsp
Cinnamon	1 tsp
Chili powder	½ tsp
Water	3 cups
Chicken broth	2 cups
Salt	1 tsp

Soup Garnish

Chicken breast (cubed, 600 g)	1 lb 5 oz
Salt	1 tsp
Olive oil cooking spray	
Almonds (sliced)	½ cup

Variations and Options

To create a great salad dressing, omit the garnish and use 2 parts soup base, 1 part olive oil and 1 part balsamic vinegar. **To create a tasty sauce, omit the garnish and use the soup base by itself.** You can garnish with green onion for a finishing touch. **To make this a lower-carb anytime meal, reduce beets to 3 cups.**

Carrot, Orange and Ginger Soup with Chicken

At Anytime Meal   **Pw** Post-workout Meal   **10** min. Preparation Time   **20** min. Cooking Time

Nutritional Information

(per serving)	large	small
Calories (k/cal)	512.3	256.1
Fat (g)	20.3	10.1
Saturated (g)	15.8	7.9
Monounsaturated (g)	2.3	1.1
Polyunsaturated (g)	0.8	0.4
omega-3 (g)	0.1	0.0
omega-6 (g)	0.8	0.4
Carbohydrates (g)	38.3	19.1
fiber (g)	6.0	3.0
sugars (g)	24.8	12.4
Protein (g)	44.3	22.1

IMPORTANT: Refer to page 266 for instructions on blending hot mixtures.

The unique combination of orange, coconut, carrots and ginger is a winning flavor. Try using purple, white or yellow carrots in this beautifully tangy soup.

Instructions

Soup Base Preheat a large pot on medium-high heat. Add 1 tablespoon of oil and then the onions and sauté until lightly browned, stirring frequently. Add the remaining oil, ginger, cinnamon and chili powder and sauté for 1 minute more, stirring constantly. Add the carrots, orange juice, coconut milk and milk. Bring to a boil. Reduce heat to medium-low and cover. When the milk begins to boil, reduce heat immediately to a simmer to avoid boiling over. Simmer until carrots are soft (about 10 minutes). Let mixture cool for a few minutes. Add salt and pepper and purée with a blender or food processor until smooth and then pour back into the pot.

Soup Garnish Season chicken with salt. Preheat a large non-stick frying pan on medium heat and lightly coat with spray. Sauté chicken until lightly browned and completely cooked (cooking in smaller batches and re-spraying the pan if needed). Add the chicken to the soup base, reheat on medium and serve. To maintain the tenderness of the meat, avoid bringing the soup to a boil after the chicken has been added. **Serves 4 large or 8 small.**

Soup Base

Coconut oil or butter	**2 tbsp**
Onion (rough chopped)	**1½ cups**
Fresh ginger (grated or chopped)	**1 tbsp**
Cinnamon	**1 tsp**
Chili powder	**½ tsp**
Baby carrots	**6 cups**
Freshly squeezed orange juice	**¾ cup**
Coconut milk	**1 cup**
Low-fat milk	**3 cups**
Salt	**1 tsp**
Pepper	**½ tsp**

Soup Garnish

Chicken breast (cubed, 600 g)	**1 lb 5 oz**
Salt	**1 tsp**
Olive oil cooking spray	

Variations and Options

For a great salad dressing, use 2 parts carrot soup base, 1 part olive oil and 1 part lime juice. **For a tasty sauce, omit the garnish and use the soup base by itself.** For added flavor and color, garnish with thinly sliced green onion. **If you prefer a chunky soup, serve without puréeing.** To make this a lower-carb anytime meal, reduce orange juice by ½ cup and replace with water.

Curry Lentil Chicken Soup

At	Pw	10 min.	20 min.
Anytime Meal	Post-workout Meal	Preparation Time	Cooking Time

Nutritional Information

(per serving)	large	small
Calories (k/cal)	536.3	268.1
Fat (g)	17.3	8.6
Saturated (g)	4.5	2.3
Monounsaturated (g)	3.8	1.9
Polyunsaturated (g)	6.8	3.4
omega-3 (g)	0.2	0.1
omega-6 (g)	6.3	3.1
Carbohydrates (g)	42.8	21.4
fiber (g)	18.8	9.4
sugars (g)	5.3	2.6
Protein (g)	52.5	26.3

Lentils, veggies and spices infuse this soup with nutrition and flavor excellence. Here's yet another way to enjoy chicken soup.

Instructions

Soup Base Bring water to a boil in a large pot and add the lentils and salt. Reduce heat, cover and simmer for 5 minutes. Strain any excess water. Combine the cooked lentils with the chicken broth in the pot. Preheat a large non-stick frying pan on medium heat. Add the oil, onions, peppers, carrots and garlic to the pan and sauté until the onions are lightly browned, stirring occasionally. Add the curry powder and pepper and sauté for 1 minute more. Add the vegetables to the pot with the lentils and broth.

Soup Garnish Season the chicken with salt and pepper. Preheat a large non-stick frying pan on medium heat and lightly coat with spray. Sauté chicken (in smaller batches if necessary) until lightly browned and completely cooked (re-spraying if needed between batches). Add to soup base. Bring mixture to a simmer on medium. To maintain the tenderness of the meat, avoid bringing the soup to a boil after the chicken has been added. Remove from heat and add the green onions and pine nuts just before serving. **Serves 4 large or 8 small.**

Soup Base

Water	2 cups
Red lentils (rinsed)	1 cup
Salt	½ tsp
Chicken broth	4 cups
Coconut oil or butter	1 tbsp
Onion (diced)	1 cup
Red pepper (sliced)	1 cup
Carrot (grated)	1 cup
Fresh garlic (minced)	2 tbsp
Curry powder	2 tbsp
Pepper	½ tsp

Soup Garnish

Chicken breast (cubed, 600g)	1 lb 5 oz
Salt	1 tsp
Pepper	½ tsp
Olive oil cooking spray	
Pine nuts (raw)	½ cup
Green onion (thin sliced)	½ cup

Variations and Options

For a nutty variety, substitute sunflower seeds for pine nuts. **For some veggie variety, substitute the vegetables with seasonal produce.**

To make a miso version of this soup, substitute the curry powder with 3 tablespoons of miso paste. **To make this a lower-carb anytime meal, reduce lentils by ½ cup.**

Butternut Squash and Turkey Soup

At Anytime Meal   **Pw** Post-workout Meal   **10** min. Preparation Time   **40** min. Cooking Time

Squash is one of the healthiest veggies, with high fiber and a good profile of antioxidants, so here's how to turn it into a soup that you can enjoy in good conscience.

Nutritional Information

(per serving)	large	small
Calories (k/cal)	439.5	219.8
Fat (g)	19.5	9.8
Saturated (g)	7.5	3.8
Monounsaturated (g)	6.0	3.0
Polyunsaturated (g)	3.8	1.9
omega-3 (g)	0.3	0.1
omega-6 (g)	3.5	1.8
Carbohydrates (g)	28.5	14.3
fiber (g)	6.0	3.0
sugars (g)	5.3	2.6
Protein (g)	37.5	18.8

Instructions

Soup Base Preheat large pot on medium-high heat. Add coconut oil and squash; sauté until lightly browned. Add onion, ginger, garlic, cinnamon, cumin, nutmeg and 2 tablespoons of broth; sauté for 2 minutes more, stirring constantly. Add remaining vegetable broth and water and bring to a boil. Cover, reduce heat and simmer until squash is soft (approx. 30 minutes). Prep garnish while soup base is cooking. Let soup cool for a few minutes. Purée in blender or food processor until smooth and pour back into pot.

Soup Garnish Season turkey with salt and pepper. Preheat large non-stick frying pan on medium heat and lightly coat with spray. Sauté turkey (cooking in smaller batches and re-spraying pan if needed) until lightly browned and completely cooked. Add cooked turkey and chopped cilantro to soup base. Reheat and serve immediately or portion soup into storage containers. To maintain tenderness of meat, avoid bringing soup to a boil after meat has been added. **Serves 4 large or 8 small.**

Soup Base

Coconut oil or butter	1 tbsp
Butternut squash (skin removed, rough chopped)	5 cups
Onion (rough chopped)	1 cup
Fresh ginger (grated or chopped)	1 tbsp
Fresh garlic (minced)	1 tbsp
Cinnamon	1 tsp
Cumin	1 tsp
Nutmeg	½ tsp
Vegetable broth	5 cups
Water	1 cup

Soup Garnish

Ground turkey (740 g)	1 lb 10 oz
Salt	2 tsp
Pepper	½ tsp
Olive oil cooking spray	
Cilantro (chopped)	¼ cup

Variations and Options

To make a salad dressing, omit the soup garnish and use 2 parts soup base, 1 part olive oil and 1 part apple cider vinegar. **For a tasty sauce, omit the soup garnish and use the base by itself.** There are many varieties of summer and winter squash. Try substituting the butternut squash with seasonal squash. **To serve a chunky version of this soup, chop the onions and squash smaller and skip puréeing.** To make this a lower-carb anytime meal, reduce squash to 4 cups. **To make this a higher-carb post-workout option, substitute yams for squash or simply add some whole grain bread on the side.**

Sweet Green Pea Soup with Smoked Chicken

		10 min.	10 min.
At	Pw		
Anytime Meal	Post-workout Meal	Preparation Time	Cooking Time

Nutritional Information

(per serving)	large	small
Calories (k/cal)	530.3	265.1
Fat (g)	17.3	8.6
Saturated (g)	6.0	3.0
Monounsaturated (g)	6.8	3.4
Polyunsaturated (g)	3.0	1.5
omega-3 (g)	0.2	0.1
omega-6 (g)	2.6	1.3
Carbohydrates (g)	33.8	16.9
fiber (g)	9.0	4.5
sugars (g)	11.3	5.6
Protein (g)	60.0	30.0

IMPORTANT: Refer to page 266 for instructions on blending hot mixtures.

Split pea soup, while tasty, usually has a "mushy" texture. For those of you who can't stand this, we've created a split pea soup that's fresh and sweet without the mush. The combination of peas, chicken, cashews and cauliflower makes this soup a taste, texture and nutritional winner.

Instructions

Soup Base Preheat a large pot on medium heat. Add oil and onions, sautéing until lightly browned. Stir frequently. Add garlic, pepper, cumin and 2 tablespoons of broth, and sauté for 1 minute more. Now add the remaining vegetable broth and bring to a boil. Add the peas, bring back to a boil. Let mixture cool for a few minutes. Purée with a blender or food processor until smooth and then pour back into the pot. Reheat before serving.

Soup Garnish Preheat a non-stick frying pan on medium heat and lightly coat with spray. Add the cauliflower and water, sautéing until lightly browned. Add the cashew, cinnamon, paprika, salt and pepper and sauté for 2 minutes more. Add the garnish and chicken to the soup and it's ready to enjoy.
Serves 3 large or 5 small.

Soup Base

Coconut oil or butter	1 tbsp
Onion (rough chopped)	1½ cups
Fresh garlic (minced)	2 tbsp
Pepper	½ tsp
Cumin	1 tsp
Vegetable broth	3 cups
Organic peas (frozen)	3½ cups

Soup Garnish

Olive oil cooking spray	
Cauliflower (cut into small pieces)	2 cups
Water	2 tbsp
Raw cashew	½ cup
Cinnamon	1 tsp
Paprika	1 tsp
Salt	1 pinch
Pepper	1 pinch
Smoked chicken breast (deli meat, 600 g)	1 lb 5 oz

Variations and Options

For a creamier soup, use milk in place of the vegetable broth. **For a great salad dressing, omit the soup garnish and use 2 parts pea soup, 1 part olive oil and 1 part lemon juice.** For a tasty sauce, omit the garnish and use the soup base by itself. **For an alternate meat source, substitute prepared crab for the chicken.** To create a lower-carb anytime meal, reduce peas to 2½ cups.

Chicken Taco Salad

Anytime
Meal

3 min.
Preparation
Time

8 min.
Cooking
Time

This crunchy, Mexican-inspired salad is sure to please, as it combines freshness and flavor. Whether you try it as a meal or as a side dish, you'll love the taste and the crunch – especially combined with our Mexi-Mix dressing.

Nutritional Information

(per serving)	large	small
Calories (k/cal)	526.1	263.0
Fat (g)	21.0	10.5
Saturated (g)	15.0	7.5
Monounsaturated (g)	2.7	1.4
Polyunsaturated (g)	1.0	0.5
omega-3 (g)	0.6	0.3
omega-6 (g)	0.6	0.3
Carbohydrates (g)	25.5	12.7
fiber (g)	5.0	2.5
sugars (g)	5.6	2.8
Protein (g)	58.8	29.4

Instructions

Sauté chicken (refer to instructions on page 112). Set aside to cool. Add oil and onions to the pan, stirring frequently until onions are lightly browned, then add tomato and corn. Cook for 1 minute more. Remove from heat and set aside to cool. Combine all ingredients in a large mixing bowl. Drizzle one serving of your favorite dressing on the salad and serve.

Serves 1 large or 2 small.

Dressing

Mexi-Mix
(recipe on pg.244)

Salad

Boneless skinless chicken breast (170 g)	**6 oz**
Coconut oil or butter	**1 tbsp**
Onion (thin sliced)	**¼ cup**
Tomato (large diced)	**½ cup**
Corn (frozen or canned)	**¼ cup**
Fresh spinach	**3 cups**
Whole wheat tortilla chips or brown rice chips (crushed)	**⅓ cup**
Aged white cheddar (grated)	**½ cup**

Variations and Options

We recommend using ¼ cup of Mexi-Mix Dressing (pg.244). **For a great post-workout option, add ¾ - 1 cup of baked tortilla chips.** For some veggie variety, add in shitake mushrooms or sweet peppers. **You can substitute chicken with extra-lean cooked ground beef for a traditional taco salad.**

Healthy Chicken Caesar

Pw

Post-workout
Meal

5 min.
Preparation
Time

5 min.
Cooking
Time

Nutritional Information

(per serving)	large	small
Calories (k/cal)	622.3	311.1
Fat (g)	10.8	5.4
Saturated (g)	5.2	2.6
Monounsaturated (g)	2.7	1.4
Polyunsaturated (g)	0.9	0.4
omega-3 (g)	0.7	0.3
omega-6 (g)	0.8	0.4
Carbohydrates (g)	60.7	30.4
fiber (g)	16.6	8.3
sugars (g)	3.6	1.8
Protein (g)	70.5	35.2

Traditional caesar salad is simple and rich although, owing to the dressing, it's one of the most calorie-dense and fattening salads on earth. Therefore, to remedy this fatal flaw, we've created a Healthy Chicken Caesar – sans the thick, high-fat sauce. We can't claim that it's as rich as a traditional caesar salad, but we can say it tastes great and is good for you – especially when combined with our Caesar Vinaigrette.

Instructions

Sauté chicken (refer to instructions on page 112). Set aside to cool. Combine all ingredients in a large mixing bowl. Drizzle one serving of your favorite dressing on the salad and serve.

Serves 1 large or 2 small.

Dressing

Caesar Vinaigrette
(recipe on pg.244)

Salad

Boneless skinless chicken breast (cubed, 170 g)	**6 oz**
Romaine lettuce (torn into small pieces)	**3 cups**
Parmesan cheese (grated)	**¼ cup**
Navy beans (cooked or canned, drained)	**1 cup**
Onion (thin sliced)	**¼ cup**

Variations and Options

We recommend 2 tablespoons of Caesar Vinaigrette dressing. **For a great post-workout meal, serve with a ½ cup of whole wheat croutons.** You can substitute romaine lettuce with spinach for a healthy variation. **For some additional protein, eggs are a great option. Fry up 2 whole omega-3 eggs with 3 egg whites and serve atop the salad.** If you want to make up a batch of salad for later, keep in mind that the lettuce will keep longer if you tear it with your hands instead of chopping with a knife.

Quinoa, Apple and Walnut Salad with Turkey Sausage

Pw
Post-workout Meal

5 min.
Preparation Time

20 min.
Cooking Time

Nutritional Information

(per serving)	large	small
Calories (k/cal)	730.5	365.2
Fat (g)	36.8	18.4
Saturated (g)	7.8	3.9
Monounsaturated (g)	7.3	3.6
Polyunsaturated (g)	17.6	8.8
omega-3 (g)	3.0	1.5
omega-6 (g)	14.5	7.2
Carbohydrates (g)	61.6	30.8
fiber (g)	9.5	4.8
sugars (g)	19.5	9.8
Protein (g)	38.2	19.1

This salad is simple, unique and delicious. Note the complementary flavors of quinoa, turkey sausage, spinach, apples and walnuts – not a combination you see every day. Eaten without dressing, this meal tastes incredible. Add the Spicy Apple Vinaigrette and you've just taken it to another level.

Instructions

Bring ½ a cup of water to a boil in a small pot on high heat. Add quinoa. Reduce heat to medium-low and cook for 12 minutes. Remove from heat, drain and set aside to cool. Cook turkey sausage in large pot of simmering water for 10-20 minutes depending on the thickness. Remove from water and then preheat a non-stick pan on medium heat. Lightly coat with spray and then add the turkey sausage. Sauté the sausage until lightly browned all around. Set aside to cool, then slice into medallions. Combine all ingredients in a large mixing bowl. Drizzle one serving of your favorite dressing on the salad and serve. **Serves 1 large or 2 small.**

Dressing

Spicy Apple Vinaigrette
(recipe on pg.246)

Salad

Water	½ cup
Quinoa	¼ cup
Turkey sausage (170 g)	6 oz
Apple (cored, large diced)	1 cup
Walnut (crushed)	¼ cup
Fresh spinach	3 cups

Variations and Options

We recommend 2 tablespoons of Spicy Apple Vinaigrette dressing. **You can garnish this salad with grated parmesan or aged white cheddar.** For some veggie variety, you can omit the spinach, and add ¼ cup of diced red pepper. **For enhanced flavor, add sautéed onion to the salad.**

8

Seafood

With all of its health benefits, we simply can't afford not to eat seafood on a regular basis. The fats in fish have been shown to decrease inflammation and pain, protect against free-radical damage, improve blood lipids (including cholesterol and triglycerides), improve heart health, decrease cancer risk, reduce body fat, and more. And here's another reason to eat seafood: to feed that fatty organ between your ears. Seafood provides brain-specific nutrition, particularly in the form of DHA.

Beyond all of the health benefits there is, of course, another reason we've included the following seafood recipes – they taste great!

As with the meat section, keep in mind that for many of the seafood recipes, the seafood takes center stage. In other words, for many of the recipes, the instructions are only provided for the fish prep. We did it this way for a good reason – so that each seafood recipe could be paired with the perfect anytime or post-workout side dish. This ultimately gives you more variety and additional dining options.

And to help you along in your meal pairings, we've provided our recommendations for ideal combinations. So, all you've got to do is prepare the fish and the referenced side dish and you're set. Of course, these recommended side dishes are just suggestions. You can get creative, mixing and matching your seafood and accompaniments as you like.

Garlic Sautéed Prawns

At with Spiced Cauliflower Sauté (pg.190)
Pw with Chunky Tomato Spelt (pg.210)

2 min.
Preparation Time

5 min.
Cooking Time

Nutritional Information

(per serving)	large	small
Calories (k/cal)	295.3	147.6
Fat (g)	15.9	8.0
Saturated (g)	12.1	6.0
Monounsaturated (g)	1.2	0.6
Polyunsaturated (g)	1.4	0.7
omega-3 (g)	0.0	0.0
omega-6 (g)	0.0	0.0
Carbohydrates (g)	3.1	1.5
fiber (g)	0.1	0.1
sugars (g)	2.6	1.3
Protein (g)	34.9	17.4

Prawns are shrimp-like crustaceans that are much larger in size than regular shrimp and are often served in finer restaurants. The versatile prawn is used in the cuisine of many cultures, as it pairs well with a variety of seasoning combinations. In this recipe, we add a coconut and garlic flavor when sautéing the prawns and pair them up with either a delicious cauliflower sauté (anytime) or a tomato spelt (post-workout).

Instructions

Season the prawns with the chili powder and salt. Preheat a non-stick frying pan on medium heat. Add the oil and seasoned prawns and sauté until just cooked through and lightly browned, stirring frequently. Add the garlic and sauté for 1 minute more, stirring constantly. Add the orange juice and serve. **Serves 1 large or 2 small.**

Prawns (raw, peeled, 170 g)	6 oz
Chili powder	¼ tsp
Salt	¼ tsp
Coconut oil or butter	1 tbsp
Fresh garlic (minced)	1 tsp
Orange juice	2 tbsp

Variations and Options

For some added flavor and texture, add chopped shallots and parsley along with the garlic.

Sautéed Salmon

 with Spiced Cauliflower Sauté (pg.190)

with Soy Ginger Lentils with Baby Bok Choy (pg.204)

2 min.
Preparation Time

8 min.
Cooking Time

Nutritional Information

(per serving)	large	small
Calories (k/cal)	301.4	150.7
Fat (g)	10.8	5.4
Saturated (g)	1.7	0.8
Monounsaturated (g)	3.6	1.8
Polyunsaturated (g)	4.3	2.2
omega-3 (g)	2.9	1.5
omega-6 (g)	0.7	0.4
Carbohydrates (g)	17.3	8.7
fiber (g)	0.0	0.0
sugars (g)	17.3	8.7
Protein (g)	33.8	16.9

TIP: A little finely chopped tropical fruit salsa (pg.264) makes a great garnish.

The health praises of wild salmon have been sung for years now due to the high protein and omega-3 profile of this fatty fish. So, with this recipe, we provide a healthy dose of good fats along with a delicious blend of seasonings. When served with Spiced Cauliflower Sauté (anytime) or Soy Ginger Lentils (post-workout), this recipe tastes amazing.

Instructions

Sprinkle both sides of the salmon with turmeric, fennel, salt and pepper. Preheat a non-stick frying pan on medium heat, lightly coat with spray and place the fillet in the pan. Cook until lightly browned (3-4 minutes) and then gently flip. Drizzle the honey into the pan. Cook until second side is lightly browned (3-4 minutes) and serve. **Serves 1 large or 2 small.**

Salmon fillet (skinless, 170 g)	**6 oz**
Turmeric	**1 pinch**
Fennel (ground)	**1 pinch**
Salt	**1 pinch**
Pepper	**1 pinch**
Olive oil cooking spray	
Honey	**1 tsp**

Variations and Options

For a different flavor, omit the suggested spices and honey. Instead, whisk together 2 tablespoons plain non-fat yogurt, 2 teaspoons lemon juice, 2 teaspoons dill, 1 tablespoon honey and a pinch of chili powder, salt and pepper. After you flip the salmon, thoroughly coat the top with mixture and finish cooking.

Lemon-Poached Cod

 with Stuffed Zucchini (pg.186)
 with Curry Coconut Chickpeas (pg.200)

3 min. 6 min.

Preparation Time Cooking Time

Nutritional Information

(per serving)	large	small
Calories (k/cal)	157.8	78.9
Fat (g)	1.2	0.6
Saturated (g)	0.2	0.1
Monounsaturated (g)	0.2	0.1
Polyunsaturated (g)	0.4	0.2
omega-3 (g)	0.0	0.0
omega-6 (g)	0.0	0.0
Carbohydrates (g)	6.0	3.0
fiber (g)	0.7	0.4
sugars (g)	2.4	1.2
Protein (g)	30.8	15.4

Cod is a mild-flavored, low-fat fish that's rich in protein, with a unique amino acid profile shown to improve carbohydrate tolerance. In this recipe, we'll teach you how to poach cod, ending up with a tender, flaky fish that goes great with zucchini (anytime) or chickpeas (post-workout).

Instructions

Bring all ingredients, except the cod, to a boil in a small pot and then reduce heat to medium. Simmer for 5 minutes to infuse the flavors together and then place the fish into the poaching liquid. Poach for 4-7 minutes, depending on the thickness, and then gently remove from the liquid with a slotted spatula and serve. **Serves 1 large or 2 small.**

Onion (small dice)	¼ cup
Water	2 cups
Lemon juice	2 tbsp
Fennel	1 tsp
Salt	½ tsp
Cod fillets (170 g)	6 oz

Variations and Options

For a richer flavor, poach in veggie broth, orange juice or a 50/50 mixture of water and coconut milk. **If poaching more than one serving of fish, double or triple the poaching liquid and use an appropriate sized pot.** If you'd like to vary your fish type, try substituting the cod with halibut or sole and prepare the same way.

Steamed Halibut

At with Sesame Broccoli with Feta (pg.188)
Pw with Fruity Cashew Quinoa (pg.208)

2
min.

Preparation
Time

10
min.

Cooking
Time

Steaming works well for a variety of fish, preserving the nutritional value of the cut without adding additional fat. In this recipe, we'll teach you how to steam halibut for a perfect piece of fish. Served with broccoli (anytime) or quinoa (post-workout), you'll absolutely love this fish.

Halibut (skinless, 170 g)	6 oz
Salt	1 pinch
Pepper	1 pinch
Coriander	1 pinch
Lemon or lime juice	1 squeeze

Nutritional Information

(per serving)	large	small
Calories (k/cal)	176.5	88.3
Fat (g)	3.9	1.9
Saturated (g)	0.6	0.3
Monounsaturated (g)	1.3	0.6
Polyunsaturated (g)	1.2	0.6
omega-3 (g)	0.1	0.1
omega-6 (g)	0.1	0.0
Carbohydrates (g)	0.0	0.0
fiber (g)	0.0	0.0
sugars (g)	0.0	0.0
Protein (g)	35.4	17.7

Instructions

Season the halibut on both sides with salt, pepper and coriander. Select appropriate sized pot for your steamer basket. Place halibut on a piece of wax paper and then in the steamer basket and then into the pot. Cover with a tight-fitting lid and steam until cooked through (5-10 minutes depending on thickness). Carefully remove from pot and squeeze fresh lemon or lime juice on to the fish. **Serves 1 large or 2 small.**

TIP: To check if the fish is done, stick a knife or a fork into the thickest portion of the fish and gently pull apart. Fish should flake apart easily.

Variations and Options

Steaming works well for a range of fish. **For some fish variety, try substituting the halibut with cod, sole or prawns.**

Marinated Tuna Steak

At with Sesame Broccoli with Feta (pg.188)
Pw with Soy Ginger Lentils with Baby Bok Choy (pg.204)

2 min.	4 hrs.	6 min.
Preparation Time	Marinating Time	Cooking Time

Nutritional Information

(per serving)	large	small
Calories (k/cal)	230.2	115.1
Fat (g)	2.1	1.0
Saturated (g)	0.5	0.3
Monounsaturated (g)	0.3	0.2
Polyunsaturated (g)	0.6	0.3
omega-3 (g)	0.0	0.0
omega-6 (g)	0.0	0.0
Carbohydrates (g)	1.7	0.8
fiber (g)	0.0	0.0
sugars (g)	0.0	0.0
Protein (g)	51.2	25.6

Tuna is a popular salt-water fish that's pink in color due to its high content of myoglobin, an oxygen-binding molecule in muscle. This allows tuna to swim very fast (some tuna have been clocked at over 48 mph). While eating this recipe probably won't make you any faster, you'll definitely enjoy the taste. Paired with Sesame Broccoli and Feta (anytime) or Soy Ginger Lentils with Baby Bok Choy (post-workout), this is a meal you'll sprint to.

Instructions

Mix the shallots, basil, salt, chili powder, olive oil and lemon juice in a small bowl and then coat the tuna and let marinate for 4 hours in the fridge. Turn every hour. Preheat a non-stick frying pan on medium heat. Lightly coat with spray and place tuna into the pan. Cook and turn until lightly browned on all sides. Tuna should still be rare in the middle. **Serves 1 large or 2 small.**

Shallots (fine dice)	1 tbsp
Fresh basil (finely chopped)	1 tbsp
Salt	2 pinches
Chili powder	1 pinch
Extra virgin olive oil	1 tbsp
Lemon juice	2 tsp
Albacore or yellowfin tuna steak (170 g)	6 oz
Olive oil cooking spray	

Variations and Options

For a quicker meal prep time, you can skip the marinating period and fry this up immediately.

Prawn Cakes

At with Portobello Pizzas (pg.184)
Pw with Curry Coconut Chickpeas (pg.200)

10 min.
Preparation Time

15 min.
Cooking Time

Crab cakes are a popular dinner special at many seafood restaurants for good reason – they taste awesome. In this take on the classic crab cake, we've used prawns instead of crab. Paired with Portobello Pizzas (anytime) or Curry Coconut Chickpeas (post-workout), this is a great dinner surprise whether dining alone or with guests.

Nutritional Information

(per serving)	large	small
Calories (k/cal)	462.5	231.3
Fat (g)	12.6	6.3
Saturated (g)	6.3	3.1
Monounsaturated (g)	1.4	0.7
Polyunsaturated (g)	2.3	1.2
omega-3 (g)	0.0	0.0
omega-6 (g)	0.2	0.1
Carbohydrates (g)	8.7	4.4
fiber (g)	0.8	0.4
sugars (g)	1.1	0.5
Protein (g)	78.6	39.3

Instructions

Dry any moisture from the prawns with a paper towel and return to the fridge. Preheat a non-stick frying pan on medium heat, lightly coat with spray and add the leeks and mushrooms. Sauté until the leeks are lightly browned. Remove mixture from pan and completely chill in the fridge. Add all the ingredients, including the prawns, to a food processor and purée until combined, but not smooth. Preheat oven to 350°F. Preheat a non-stick frying pan on medium heat, lightly coat with spray. Scoop heaping tablespoons of the mixture into your hands and form into round cakes approximately 2 inch diameter by ¾ inch. Add to pan, leaving a little room in between each cake. Sauté until lightly browned, flip and then brown the other side (2-3 minutes per side). Transfer to a baking sheet and place in the oven. Bake until cooked through (8-10 minutes). Serve and enjoy. **Serves 2 large or 4 small.**

Chilled prawns (raw, peeled, 340 g)	12 oz
Olive oil cooking spray	
Leeks (sliced)	¼ cup
Mushrooms (sliced)	½ cup
Coconut milk	2 tbsp
Egg whites	2
Fresh garlic (minced)	2 tsp
Fresh cilantro (chopped)	1 tbsp
Salt	¼ tsp
Pepper	¼ tsp

Variations and Options

For some flavor variation, add ginger instead of garlic. **For some spice variation, fennel and chili powder are great together instead of cilantro You could also try 2 teaspoons of curry powder instead of cilantro.**

Tuna Salad Wrap

Anytime
Meal

10
min.

Preparation
Time

Nutritional Information

(per serving)	large	small
Calories (k/cal)	623.8	311.9
Fat (g)	31.1	15.6
Saturated (g)	3.7	1.9
Monounsaturated (g)	18.3	9.2
Polyunsaturated (g)	3.0	1.5
omega-3 (g)	0.3	0.2
omega-6 (g)	1.4	0.7
Carbohydrates (g)	37.1	18.5
fiber (g)	11.6	5.8
sugars (g)	8.1	4.1
Protein (g)	48.9	24.4

If you're looking for a quick recipe to go, give these mayo-free tuna salad wraps a try. They're fast, loaded with veggies, and taste great. Just grab 'em and head out the door.

Instructions

Combine all the ingredients in a mixing bowl, except the wrap, and stir until well combined. Place half of the mixture in the center of a large whole wheat tortilla. Fold the bottom about ¼ of the way up. Fold over each of the ends and then roll tightly from the bottom to the top. Serve and enjoy or take to go. If you can't fit all the ingredients in the wrap, then serve the remaining mixture as a side salad. **Serves 1 large or 2 small.**

Tuna	**1 can**
Tomato (diced)	**½ cup**
Red onion (finely diced)	**¼ cup**
Carrot (shredded)	**½ cup**
Cucumber (finely diced)	**½ cup**
Avocado (mashed with a fork)	**½**
Extra virgin olive oil	**1 tbsp**
Lemon juice	**1 tbsp**
Salt	**¼ tsp**
Pepper	**1 pinch**
Paprika	**1 pinch**
Whole wheat tortilla	**1**

Variations and Options

You can substitute the tuna with canned salmon or chicken for another quick and easy meal idea. **For an additional dressing, try using one of our homemade salad dressing suggestions instead of the olive oil and lemon juice.** Another easy way to change the flavor of this awesome wrap is by using different homemade condiments. Check out the Condiment chapter starting on page 249.

Seafood Lettuce Wrap

At

Anytime
Meal

10 min.

Preparation
Time

Lettuce wraps are the latest trend at Asian restaurants, as they're lower in calories, crunchier and more flavorful than most conventional wraps. In this recipe we've stuffed our lettuce wraps with seafood, beans and a host of veggies, and topped it all off with a tasty Asian Dressing.

Nutritional Information

(per serving)	large	small
Calories (k/cal)	514.6	257.3
Fat (g)	15.1	7.6
Saturated (g)	2.2	1.1
Monounsaturated (g)	7.7	3.8
Polyunsaturated (g)	3.2	1.6
omega-3 (g)	1.5	0.8
omega-6 (g)	1.4	0.7
Carbohydrates (g)	31.2	15.6
fiber (g)	10.4	5.2
sugars (g)	8.8	4.4
Protein (g)	63.5	31.8

Instructions

Combine the shrimp, avocado, carrots and cucumber together in a mixing bowl. Gently mix in the beans, dressing and yogurt. Lay all the lettuce leaves out on the countertop. Placing the mixture in the center of each leaf, divide evenly. Depending on the size of your leaves, you may need more or less. You can also choose to serve the remaining mixture as a side salad with the wraps. Now for the folding. Roll it up like a tortilla shell. Fold the bottom up and then fold in the two sides and roll. Serve and enjoy! **Serves 1 large or 2 small.**

Baby shrimp	**2 cups**
Avocado (small cubed)	**½ cup**
Carrots (grated)	**¼ cup**
Cucumber (grated)	**¼ cup**
Navy beans (cooked or canned, drained)	**¼ cup**
Asian Dressing (recipe on pg.242)	**2 tbsp**
Low-fat plain yogurt	**¼ cup**
Iceberg lettuce (large outer leaves)	**6**

Variations and Options

If you'd like to try a different flavor, you can substitute any of our homemade dressings for the Asian Dressing. This dish makes an easy sa ad, too. Omit the iceberg lettuce and mix all of the other ingredients with a few handfuls of spinach, toss with dressing and serve.

Creamy Cauliflower and Salmon Soup

Anytime Meal | Post-workout Meal | Preparation Time 15 min. | Cooking Time 20 min.

Cruciferous veggies have never been hidden as well as they are in this soup. Even if you're not a fan of cauliflower, you'll barely notice it in this recipe. Rich in omega-3 fats, veggies and healthy spices, this is one you're sure to love.

Nutritional Information

(per serving)	large	small
Calories (k/cal)	638.0	319.0
Fat (g)	34.0	17.0
Saturated (g)	11.0	5.5
Monounsaturated (g)	14.0	7.0
Polyunsaturated (g)	7.0	3.5
omega-3 (g)	2.5	1.2
omega-6 (g)	3.8	1.9
Carbohydrates (g)	32.0	16.0
fiber (g)	7.0	3.5
sugars (g)	20.0	10.0
Protein (g)	51.0	25.5

TIP: Refer to page 266 for instructions on blending hot mixtures.

Instructions

Soup Base Preheat a large pot on medium-high heat. Add 1 tablespoon of oil and then the onions and sauté until lightly browned, stirring frequently. Add the remaining oil, garlic, cumin, cinnamon and coriander and sauté for 1 minute more, stirring constantly. Add the cauliflower, milk and salt and bring to a boil. Reduce heat and simmer until the cauliflower is soft (10-15 minutes). When the milk begins to boil, reduce heat immediately to a simmer to avoid boiling over. Let mixture cool for a few minutes. Purée with a blender or food processor until smooth and then pour back into the pot. Reheat before serving.

Soup Garnish Preheat a large non-stick frying pan on medium heat. Lightly coat with spray and sauté the cubed salmon until lightly browned. Sauté in smaller batches and re-spray the pan if needed. Combine carrots and pecans with the soup base and simmer for 2 minutes. Add salmon to soup base and serve warm. If preparing soup in advance, chill base completely before adding the salmon to avoid over-cooking. **Serves 4 large or 8 small.**

Soup Base

Coconut oil or butter	2 tbsp
Sweet onion (rough chopped)	2 cups
Fresh garlic (minced)	2 tbsp
Cumin	½ tsp
Cinnamon	1 tsp
Coriander	1 tsp
Cauliflower (rough chopped)	5 cups
Milk	4 cups
Salt	2 tsp

Soup Garnish

Olive oil cooking spray	
Salmon (bones removed, cubed, 700 g)	1 lb 9 oz
Carrots (grated)	1 cup
Pecans (crushed)	½ cup

Variations and Options

For a great post-workout meal, add some cooked brown rice for added texture. **To create an excellent sauce, omit the soup garnish and use the base by itself.** The flavors in this soup are very neutral, so chicken, beef and tofu are excellent protein substitutes. **For added texture and amazing flavor, garnish with shredded coconut.** Use canned salmon instead of fresh to save preparation time.

Kelp, Carrot and Halibut Stew

Anytime Meal   **Post-workout Meal**   10 min. Preparation Time   20 min. Cooking Time

Nutritional Information

(per serving)	large	small
Calories (k/cal)	567.0	283.5
Fat (g)	24.0	12.0
Saturated (g)	6.8	3.4
Monounsaturated (g)	10.5	5.3
Polyunsaturated (g)	4.5	2.3
omega-3 (g)	1.0	0.5
omega-6 (g)	3.4	1.7
Carbohydrates (g)	38.3	19.1
fiber (g)	5.3	2.6
sugars (g)	5.3	2.6
Protein (g)	49.5	24.8

If you've never tried kelp, this is your chance. Kelp and other seaweeds are mineral-rich and contain a healthy dose of iodine, critical for optimal thyroid hormone function. Plus, when prepared properly, they can add a unique taste to your dishes. In this soup, the combination of kelp, quinoa, cashews and halibut provides amazing flavor and texture.

Instructions

Soup Base Preheat a large pot on medium-high heat. Add oil and onions, and sauté until lightly browned, stirring frequently. Add garlic, paprika and 2 tablespoons of broth, and sauté for 1 minute more, stirring constantly. Now add 3 cups of the broth and bring to a boil. Reduce heat to medium. Add the quinoa and simmer for 13 minutes. Add the carrots, cashews and kelp and simmer for 2 minutes more. Remove from heat.

Soup Garnish Season halibut with salt and pepper. Preheat a large non-stick frying pan on medium heat. Lightly coat with spray and sauté halibut until lightly browned, then remove from the pan and set aside. Sauté in smaller batches and re-spray the pan if needed. Add halibut and remaining vegetable broth to soup base and reheat on medium to serve warm. If preparing soup in advance, chill base completely before adding the halibut to avoid over-cooking. **Serves 4 large or 8 small.**

Soup Base

Coconut oil or butter	1 tbsp
Red onion (thin sliced)	1 cup
Fresh garlic (minced)	2 tbsp
Paprika	1 tsp
Vegetable broth	5 cups
Quinoa (uncooked)	½ cup
Carrot (grated)	1 cup
Raw cashews (chopped)	1 cup
Dried kelp (cut into small pieces)	1 cup

Soup Garnish

Halibut (skinned, cubed, 700 g)	1 lb 9 oz
Salt	1 pinch
Pepper	1 pinch
Olive oil cooking spray	

Variations and Options

Try substituting the carrots with whichever vegetables are in season. Broccoli, cauliflower, corn and cabbage are all great examples. **Snapper, turkey sausage, chicken and tofu are great substitutes for the halibut.** For a lower-carb anytime meal, reduce quinoa to ¼ cup.

Miso Corn Chowder with Salmon

At	Pw	10 min.	20 min.
Anytime Meal	Post-workout Meal	Preparation Time	Cooking Time

Nutritional Information

(per serving)	large	small
Calories (k/cal)	716.0	358.0
Fat (g)	40.0	20.0
Saturated (g)	23.0	11.5
Monounsaturated (g)	9.0	4.5
Polyunsaturated (g)	5.0	2.5
omega-3 (g)	2.4	1.2
omega-6 (g)	1.8	0.9
Carbohydrates (g)	40.0	20.0
fiber (g)	7.0	3.5
sugars (g)	7.0	3.5
Protein (g)	49.0	24.5

TIP: Refer to page 266 for instructions on blending hot mixtures.

Here's a healthy fish chowder with our salty miso broth. The puréed navy beans give this soup its thick base, and the salmon makes it an omega-3 all-star.

Instructions

Soup Base Preheat a large pot on medium-high heat. Add oil and onions and sauté until onions are lightly browned, stirring frequently. Then add the garlic, ginger, paprika and 1 tablespoon of the coconut milk and sauté for 1 minute more. Now add the remaining coconut milk, navy beans and Shiro miso paste. Reduce heat and simmer for a couple minutes. Stir until the miso is dissolved. Let mixture cool for a few minutes. Purée with a blender or food processor until smooth and then pour back into the pot.

Soup Garnish Season salmon with salt. Preheat a large non-stick frying pan on medium heat and lightly coat with spray. Sauté salmon until lightly browned (cooking in batches and re-spraying if needed), then remove from the pan and set aside. Give another quick spray and add the red onion and peppers to the pan and sauté for 2 minutes. Combine the sautéed vegetables, corn and cilantro with the soup base. Add salmon to soup base and reheat before serving. If preparing soup in advance, chill base completely before adding the salmon to avoid over-cooking. **Serves 4 large or 8 small.**

Soup Base

Coconut oil or butter	1 tbsp
Yellow onion (large diced)	1 cup
Ginger (grated or chopped)	1 tbsp
Fresh garlic (minced)	1 tbsp
Paprika	1 tsp
Coconut milk (1 can)	1½ cups
White navy beans (cooked or canned, drained, 1 can)	1½ cups
Shiro miso paste	5 tbsp
Water	2 cups
Salt	1 tsp
Pepper	½ tsp

Soup Garnish

Wild fresh salmon (skin removed, 1-inch cubed, 700 g)	1 lb 9 oz
Salt	1 pinch
Olive oil cooking spray	
Red onion (sliced)	1 cup
Red peppers (thin sliced)	1 cup
Corn (frozen)	1 cup
Cilantro (chopped)	¼ cup

Variations and Options

For an excellent sauce, omit the garnish and use the soup base by itself. **You can substitute shrimp or chicken for the salmon if you'd like a different protein source.** You can substitute the Shiro miso paste with curry paste if you prefer a curry instead of miso chowder. **If you'd like some veggie variety, try making the soup with different vegetables such as broccoli, cabbage and zucchini.**

Sautéed Garlic Gazpacho with Prawns

At **Pw** 10 min. 20 min.

Anytime Meal | Post-workout Meal | Preparation Time | Cooking Time

Nutritional Information

(per serving)	large	small
Calories (k/cal)	416.3	208.1
Fat (g)	17.3	8.6
Saturated (g)	2.3	1.1
Monounsaturated (g)	10.5	5.3
Polyunsaturated (g)	3.0	1.5
omega-3 (g)	1.1	0.5
omega-6 (g)	1.7	0.9
Carbohydrates (g)	28.5	14.3
fiber (g)	6.0	3.0
sugars (g)	17.3	8.6
Protein (g)	36.8	18.4

Seville, Spain gave us flamenco dancing and it gave us gazpacho. Gazpacho is a cold Spanish soup that's very refreshing on a hot day. Jumping with flavor, this gazpacho is loaded with veggies, prawns and unique spices. In the end, we're sure you'll enjoy our original gazpacho creation.

Instructions

Soup Base Preheat a non-stick frying pan on medium heat. Add 1 tablespoon of oil and then the garlic and fennel and cook until golden brown, stirring frequently. Add chili powder and honey and sauté 1 minute more. Remove from heat and add to blender or food processor. Add the remaining oil, cucumber, onion, peppers, tomatoes, basil, salt and pepper to the blender or food processor and purée until smooth.

Soup Garnish Season prawns with salt and pepper. Preheat a non-stick frying pan on medium heat. Lightly coat with spray. Add prawns and sauté, stirring frequently, until pink and cooked through. Add prawns to soup base. Transfer to storage container and chill completely. **Serves 4 large or 8 small.**

Soup Base

Extra virgin olive oil	¼ cup
Cloves of garlic (large)	8
Fennel bulb (sliced)	½ cup
Chili powder	1 tsp
Honey	2 tbsp
Cucumbers	2 cups
Red onion	¼ cup
Red peppers	2 cups
Tomatoes	5 cups
Basil	¼ cup
Salt	1 tsp
Pepper	½ tsp

Soup Garnish

Prawns (650 g)	1 lb 7 oz
Salt	1 pinch
Pepper	1 pinch
Olive oil cooking spray	

Variations and Options

For a great salad dressing, skip the shrimp and use 2 parts soup base and 1 part lemon juice. **For a great sauce, omit the garnish.** Substitute the prawns with cooked chicken for another protein option. **For a lower-carb anytime meal, reduce honey to 1 tablespoon.** For a higher-carb post-workout meal, add whole wheat croutons.

Spinach and Black Bean Soup with Prawns

At

Anytime
Meal

10
min.
Preparation
Time

10
min.
Cooking
Time

This is an awesome soup that's loaded with micronutrients, healthy fats and fiber. And while it won't win any fashion shows for its appearance, it gets perfect 10s for its amazing flavor, range of textures and nutrient profile.

Nutritional Information

(per serving)	large	small
Calories (k/cal)	630.0	315.0
Fat (g)	34.0	17.0
Saturated (g)	20.0	10.0
Monounsaturated (g)	8.0	4.0
Polyunsaturated (g)	3.0	1.5
omega-3 (g)	0.9	0.5
omega-6 (g)	2.0	1.0
Carbohydrates (g)	36.0	18.0
fiber (g)	9.0	4.5
sugars (g)	5.0	2.5
Protein (g)	45.0	22.5

Instructions

Soup Base Preheat a large pot on medium-high heat. Add oil and onions and sauté until lightly browned, stirring frequently. Add ginger, chili powder, cayenne pepper and 2 tablespoons coconut milk, and sauté for 1 minute more, stirring constantly. Add the remaining coconut milk and water and bring to a boil. Once boiling, reduce heat to low. Add the spinach, black beans, cashews and salt and remove from heat.

Soup Garnish Season prawns with salt and pepper. Preheat a non-stick frying pan on medium heat. Lightly coat with spray. Sauté prawns, stirring frequently, until pink and cooked through. Sauté in smaller batches and re-spray the pan if needed. Add prawns to soup base and serve warm. If preparing soup in advance, chill base completely before adding the prawns to avoid over-cooking. **Serves 3 large or 6 small.**

Soup Base

Coconut oil or butter	**1 tbsp**
Red onion (sliced)	**2 cups**
Ginger (minced)	**1 tbsp**
Chili powder	**1 tsp**
Cayenne pepper	**1 pinch**
Coconut milk (1 can)	**1½ cups**
Water	**1½ cups**
Baby spinach (tightly packed)	**6 cups**
Black beans (cooked or canned, drained, 1 can)	**1½ cups**
Raw cashews (chopped)	**½ cup**
Salt	**1 tsp**

Soup Garnish

Prawns (600 g)	**1 lb 5 oz**
Salt	**1 pinch**
Pepper	**1 pinch**
Olive oil cooking spray	

Variations and Options

Add in some red or yellow peppers, baby carrots and broccoli for a major vitamin boost and awesome colors. **For a great sauce, omit the garnish and purée the soup base.** Chicken, beef and tofu make wonderful substitutes for the prawns. **This recipe is rich. If you'd like to thin it out, replace the coconut milk with chicken or vegetable broth.** If you prefer your soups puréed, you can add this entire soup to the blender. It makes a wonderful creamy and rich soup.

Mixed Asian Shrimp Salad

At
Anytime
Meal

5 min.
Preparation
Time

5 min.
Cooking
Time

Using Asian cuisine as its guide, this salad uses a base of cabbage, carrots and cruciferous veggies to spotlight its main protein source – shrimp. With some crunchy cashews and our Asian Dressing, this is one salad you'll love either as a meal or as a side.

Nutritional Information

(per serving)	large	small
Calories (k/cal)	444.1	222.1
Fat (g)	18.3	9.2
Saturated (g)	3.2	1.6
Monounsaturated (g)	8.6	4.3
Polyunsaturated (g)	3.8	1.9
omega-3 (g)	0.0	0.0
omega-6 (g)	2.7	1.4
Carbohydrates (g)	26.2	13.1
fiber (g)	4.9	2.5
sugars (g)	8.9	4.5
Protein (g)	43.6	21.8

Instructions

Sauté shrimp (refer to recipe for Sautéed Prawns on page 150). Set aside to cool. Combine all ingredients in a large mixing bowl. Drizzle one serving of your favorite dressing on the salad and serve **Serves 1 large or 2 small.**

Dressing

Asian Dressing
(recipe on pg.242)

Salad

Shrimp (170 g)	**6 oz**
Cabbage (grated)	**2 cups**
Carrots (grated)	**¼ cup**
Cauliflower florets (small)	**¼ cup**
Broccoli florets (small)	**¼ cup**
Cashews (crushed)	**¼ cup**

Variations and Options

We recommend serving with 2 tablespoons of Asian Dressing (pg.242). **For a great post-workout option, serve with ½ cup cooked and chopped Soba noodles or whole wheat spaghetti.** If you're short on time, you can use pre-cooked cocktail shrimp. **You can easily substitute scallops instead of shrimp. Turkey sausage and chicken also make great substitutions.**

3-Bean Tuna Salad

Pw
Post-workout
Meal

5
min.
Preparation
Time

Nutritional Information

(per serving)	large	small
Calories (k/cal)	606.0	303.0
Fat (g)	13.5	6.7
Saturated (g)	2.2	1.1
Monounsaturated (g)	7.7	3.9
Polyunsaturated (g)	2.5	1.2
omega-3 (g)	0.5	0.2
omega-6 (g)	1.5	0.8
Carbohydrates (g)	58.9	29.4
fiber (g)	23.3	11.7
sugars (g)	1.5	0.8
Protein (g)	62.3	31.1

Most people get far too little fiber in their daily diet, so they've turned to fiber supplements. But really, there's no need for this because beans provide a ton of healthy fiber alongside a host of awesome nutrients. In this recipe, 3 different beans are used, along with creamy avocado, to dress up tuna fish. As a salad, wrap or garnish for pasta, this versatile meal is quick, easy and nutritious.

Instructions

Combine all ingredients with one serving of your favorite dressing in a large mixing bowl. **Serves 1 large or 2 small.**

Dressing

Honey Mustard Dressing
(recipe on pg.247)

Salad

Kidney beans (cooked or canned, drained)	½ cup
Navy beans (cooked or canned, drained)	⅓ cup
Black beans (cooked or canned, drained)	⅓ cup
Avocado (cubed)	½ cup
Green onions (thin sliced)	¼ cup
Tuna (canned, drained, 170 g)	5 oz

Variations and Options

We recommend 2 tablespoons of Honey Mustard Dressing (pg.247). **This is a neutral salad, so if you want more flavor, add in fresh herbs like Italian parsley, cilantro, rosemary and basil.** For a great warm entrée, sauté the tuna, beans and onion in a large non-stick frying pan. Then combine with the avocado and garnish with salad dressing.

Chickpea Tomato Salad with Salmon

Pw
Post-workout
Meal

5 min.
Preparation
Time

6 min.
Cooking
Time

Here's another simple salad that packs a major nutrient punch. With fiber from the chickpeas, vitamins and minerals from the tomatoes and onions, healthy fats from the pumpkin seeds, and a dose of omega-3s and protein from the salmon, this plate is as delicious as it is nutritious.

Dressing
Roasted Garlic Vinaigrette
(recipe on pg.244)

Nutritional Information

(per serving)	large	small
Calories (k/cal)	540.8	270.4
Fat (g)	14.8	7.4
Saturated (g)	2.3	1.1
Monounsaturated (g)	4.6	2.3
Polyunsaturated (g)	6.2	3.1
omega-3 (g)	2.9	1.5
omega-6 (g)	1.8	0.9
Carbohydrates (g)	55.4	27.7
fiber (g)	11.9	6.0
sugars (g)	5.4	2.7
Protein (g)	46.5	23.3

Instructions

Sauté salmon (refer to instructions on page 152). Set aside to cool. Combine all ingredients, except salmon, in a large mixing bowl. Drizzle one serving of your favorite dressing on the salad, place salmon on top and serve. **Serves 1 large or 2 small.**

Salad

Salmon (170 g)	6 oz
Tomato (large diced)	1 cup
Chickpeas (canned or cooked)	¾ cup
Green onion (thin sliced)	¼ cup
Fennel (thin sliced)	¼ cup
Pumpkin seeds	2 tbsp

Variations and Options

We recommend serving with 2 tablespoons of Roasted Garlic Vinaigrette (pg.244). **You can add some chopped turkey bacon to this salad for a nice treat.** For some nutty variety, you can substitute pumpkin seeds with sunflower seeds or pine nuts. **For some flavor variety, you can substitute fennel with sweet onion.** This is a neutral salad, so if you want more flavor, add in fresh herbs like Italian parsley, cilantro, rosemary and basil.

9

Accompaniments

We here at Precision Nutrition are all about helping you create your own great meal pairings. Rather than have you follow a very rigid meal template, we want to give you the tools to create unlimited meal pairings. So we've given you some great entrées in the Meat, Poultry and Seafood sections and a variety of veggie-based and grain-based side dishes that can be served with those entrées to create hundreds of great meals.

Now, we know many of you claim not to like veggies. But let's forget about Mom's boiled carrots, peas and brussel sprouts for now. Veggie torture is a thing of the past and each of these unique dishes were created for taste! Packed with nutrients and accompanied by healthy fats (nuts, seeds and oils), flavorful cheeses and spice combinations, we dare you not to enjoy these dishes.

Of special note is the fact that we've added veggies to each dish and then paired each dish with a specific entrée in the Meat, Poultry and Seafood sections. This means that most of the veggie dishes can be paired with a protein source to create a complete anytime meal. And that most of the grain/legume dishes can be paired with a protein source to create a complete post-workout meal.

Even though we've provided our thoughts on pairings, don't close the book on your own unique creations. Experiment with different proteins and accompaniments to suit your own tastes.

Also, when it comes to the veggie and grain creations, try making larger batches to save some time. Remember, you can double or triple a recipe and store it in the fridge for up to four days. Then, when it's time to eat, just reheat a serving in the microwave – or better yet, in the frying pan or oven.

Portobello Pizzas

Ideal Pairing: Baked Chicken Strips (pg.114)

At
Anytime
Meal

5 min.
Preparation
Time

10 min.
Cooking
Time

Nutritional Information

(per serving)	large	small
Calories (k/cal)	542.9	271.5
Fat (g)	31.3	15.7
Saturated (g)	6.1	3.1
Monounsaturated (g)	8.5	4.2
Polyunsaturated (g)	12.3	6.2
omega-3 (g)	0.2	0.1
omega-6 (g)	11.7	5.8
Carbohydrates (g)	38.7	19.3
fiber (g)	10.3	5.2
sugars (g)	15.4	7.7
Protein (g)	26.6	13.3

Portobello mushrooms have a very meaty texture and have a large amount or protein relative to their carbohydrate content. And as a result, portobello mushrooms are often used by vegetarians as a "meat-free meat." In this recipe, the portobellos are combined with pine nuts and parmesan cheese for a delectable treat.

Instructions

Preheat oven to 400°F. Place the mushrooms, upside down, on a baking tray and top each one evenly with salsa then pine nuts and then parmesan cheese. Bake for 10-12 minutes.

Serves 1 large or 2 small.

Portobello mushrooms (stems and gills removed, large)	3
Salsa (recipe on pg.252 or use store-bought)	1 cup
Pine nuts	¼ cup
Parmesan cheese	¼ cup

Variations and Options

For a milder flavor, try using different cheeses like swiss or cheddar. **The Tomato Vegetable Chutney (pg.260), Tropical Fruit Salsa (pg.264) and the Yummy Hummus (pg.262) all make wonderful substitutions for the regular salsa.**

Stuffed Zucchini

Ideal Pairing: Steamed Halibut (pg.156)

At

Anytime
Meal

5 min.
Preparation Time

30 min.
Cooking Time

Nutritional Information

(per serving)	large	small
Calories (k/cal)	469.2	234.6
Fat (g)	27.1	13.5
Saturated (g)	6.2	3.1
Monounsaturated (g)	12.7	6.4
Polyunsaturated (g)	6.5	3.3
omega-3 (g)	0.4	0.2
omega-6 (g)	5.7	2.9
Carbohydrates (g)	37.5	18.7
fiber (g)	10.6	5.3
sugars (g)	17.9	9.0
Protein (g)	19.0	9.5

This zucchini recipe blends together a number of potent flavors like feta cheese, shitake mushrooms, and pecans to create an awesome, nutrient-packed side dish that goes great with steamed fish. In addition to the taste and nutritional goodness, this recipe also looks really cool once plated. Enjoy.

Instructions

Preheat the oven at 375°F. Cut zucchini in half lengthwise. Using a spoon and knife (if needed) remove all the white flesh (do not discard the skin or flesh). If the green skin breaks don't worry. Preheat a large non-stick frying pan on medium heat. Lightly coat with spray and add the white zucchini flesh, onion, garlic and mushrooms. Sauté until onions are lightly browned and liquids have evaporated. Then remove from heat. Add tomato, feta cheese and pecans to the pan. Stuff the zucchini peel with the heated mixture. Reform the peel around the stuffing. Add to a baking sheet and cook in the oven for 30 minutes. Remove from oven and serve with warm tomato sauce. **Serves 1 large or 2 small.**

Zucchini (medium, halved lenghwise)	**2**
Olive oil cooking spray	
Onion (finely diced)	**¼ cup**
Fresh garlic (minced)	**1 tsp**
Shitake or portobello mushrooms (small diced)	**¼ cup**
Tomato (finely diced)	**¼ cup**
Low-fat feta cheese (crumbled)	**¼ cup**
Pecans (crushed)	**¼ cup**
Tomato sauce	**½ cup**

Variations and Options

For an anytime meal option, serve with Steamed Halibut (pg.156).

Sesame Broccoli with Feta

Ideal Pairing: Steamed Halibut (pg.156)

At
Anytime
Meal

3 min.
Preparation
Time

5 min.
Cooking
Time

Nutritional Information

(per serving)	large	small
Calories (k/cal)	442.7	221.3
Fat (g)	20.3	10.2
Saturated (g)	9.8	4.9
Monounsaturated (g)	5.4	2.7
Polyunsaturated (g)	4.1	2.0
omega-3 (g)	0.3	0.2
omega-6 (g)	2.0	1.0
Carbohydrates (g)	41.7	20.8
fiber (g)	4.0	2.0
sugars (g)	1.6	0.8
Protein (g)	23.3	11.7

In Gourmet Nutrition, we often sing the praises of broccoli because of its amazing nutritive properties. And that's why we've included it frequently in our veggie recipes. In this particular recipe, we combine sweet and salty to create a delicious veggie dish that you're sure to love.

Instructions

Steam broccoli for 4-5 minutes or until desired tenderness. Remove from pot and transfer to a mixing bowl. Combine all ingredients with the hot broccoli and toss together until combined. Serve warm. **Serves 1 large or 2 small.**

Broccoli (small florets, stems sliced)	**1½ cups**
Low-fat feta cheese (crumbled)	**½ cup**
Raisins (packed)	**¼ cup**
Lemon juice	**1 tsp**
Black sesame seeds	**1 tbsp**
Sesame seed oil	**½ tbsp**

Variations and Options

For an anytime meal option, serve with Steamed Halibut (pg.156). **If you don't like raisins, give their tart cousin 'craisins' (dried cranberries) a try.** For some cruciferous variety, use cauliflower, green beans, asparagus or carrots in place of broccoli.

Spiced Cauliflower Sauté

Ideal Pairing: Sautéed Salmon (pg.152)

At
Anytime
Meal

5 min.
Preparation
Time

8 min.
Cooking
Time

Nutritional Information

(per serving)	large	small
Calories (k/cal)	315.8	157.9
Fat (g)	19.5	9.8
Saturated (g)	1.8	0.9
Monounsaturated (g)	2.6	1.3
Polyunsaturated (g)	13.8	6.9
Omega-3 (g)	2.7	1.3
Omega-6 (g)	11.1	5.6
Carbohydrates (g)	24.5	12.2
fiber (g)	8.7	4.4
sugars (g)	10.1	5.0
Protein (g)	10.6	5.3

Like its cousin broccoli, cauliflower is a supremely nutritious cruciferous veggie that can be incorporated into many delicious veggie recipes. In this recipe, we've added the texture and omega-3 content of walnuts, the sweetness of peas, and the crunch and vitamin content of carrots for a great cauliflower sauté that you're sure to love.

Instructions

Preheat a non-stick frying pan on medium heat, lightly coat with spray and add the carrots, cauliflower and water. Cook until water evaporates and then sauté until cauliflower is lightly browned. Add the peas, walnuts, salt, pepper, cinnamon and safflower and sauté for 2 minutes more. Remove from heat, add the olive oil and serve. **Serves 1 large or 2 small.**

Olive oil cooking spray	
Baby carrots (halved)	½ cup
Cauliflower (small pieces)	1 cup
Water	¼ cup
Peas	½ cup
Walnuts	¼ cup
Salt	1 pinch
Pepper	1 pinch
Cinnamon	1 pinch
Safflower	1 pinch
Olive oil	½ tbsp

Variations and Options

For an anytime meal option, serve with Sautéed Salmon (pg.152). **To create an excellent soup, make a larger batch of this recipe and turn the leftovers into a delicious soup. All you have to do is add some vegetable broth or try a 50/50 mixture of coconut milk and water and season to taste.** For some veggie variety, substitute broccoli, green beans or asparagus for cauliflower. **To create an awesome stir-fry, add in some Stir-Fry Beef (pg.86) or Sautéed Chicken Breast (pg.112), with your favorite condiment for a great stir-fry meal.**

Sweet Balsamic Cherry Tomatoes

Ideal Pairing: The Perfect Steak (pg.88)

Anytime
Meal

2
min.

Preparation
Time

8
min.

Cooking
Time

Nutritional Information

(per serving)	large	small
Calories (k/cal)	435.3	217.6
Fat (g)	36.6	18.3
Saturated (g)	3.5	1.8
Monounsaturated (g)	16.2	8.1
Polyunsaturated (g)	12.9	6.5
Omega-3 (g)	0.1	0.0
Omega-6 (g)	11.2	5.6
Carbohydrates (g)	21.9	10.9
fiber (g)	1.2	0.6
sugars (g)	18.5	9.3
Protein (g)	4.7	2.3

Tomatoes are another colorful veggie rich in antioxidants. Lycopene, a unique chemical in tomatoes, may cut cancer and cardiovascular disease risk and improve skin health, among other things. So why not incorporate this important nutrient in style – with a delicious balsamic sauce? In this recipe, the sweetness of the tomatoes is enhanced with honey, and pine nuts are added for a crunchy texture.

Instructions

Preheat a non-stick frying pan on medium heat. Add oil, vinegar, honey, tomatoes, pine nuts, salt and pepper and sauté until the tomatoes are hot to the touch. Remove tomatoes from pan, leaving the sauce and pine nuts. Continue cooking until the sauce begins to thicken. Pour the sauce over the tomatoes and serve. **Serves 1 large or 2 small.**

Extra virgin olive oil	1 tbsp
Balsamic vinegar	1 tbsp
Pure honey	1 tbsp
Cherry tomatoes (halved)	1½ cups
Pine nuts	¼ cup
Salt	2 pinches
Pepper	1 pinch

Variations and Options

For an anytime meal, serve with The Perfect Steak (pg.88). **To create an awesome soup, make a larger batch of this recipe, purée the leftovers and serve. Add in ¼ - ½ cup coconut milk for a thick creamy tomato soup.** To create a nice tomato sauce, purée half the mixture in a blender and then return to the pan. This creates a rich sauce with a wonderful consistency. For a creamier sauce, add a tablespoon or two of coconut milk. **Grape tomatoes are a great substitute for cherry tomatoes.**

Sautéed Spinach with Roasted Garlic
Ideal Pairing: Stir-Fry Beef (pg.86)

At

Anytime Meal

8 min.
Preparation Time

30 min.
Cooking Time

Nutritional Information

(per serving)	large	small
Calories (k/cal)	476.8	238.4
Fat (g)	35.2	17.6
Saturated (g)	18.1	9.1
Monounsaturated (g)	12.8	6.4
Polyunsaturated (g)	2.4	1.2
omega-3 (g)	0.4	0.2
omega-6 (g)	1.8	0.9
Carbohydrates (g)	22.8	11.4
fiber (g)	5.3	2.7
sugars (g)	3.0	1.5
Protein (g)	17.3	8.7

The roasted garlic and spinach combination is a favorite worldwide. Not only are the flavors complementary, these two foods pack quite a nutrient punch. Spinach carries with it a huge alkaline potential and a ton of vitamins and minerals, while garlic has been shown to reduce heart disease risk, regulate blood sugar, and improve cold symptoms.

Instructions

Roasted Garlic Preheat oven to 325°F. Cut the tops off of the garlic bulb so that most of the cloves are exposed, and place on a cookie sheet or casserole dish. Drizzle a little melted butter on top of each clove and then place in the oven. Roast until cloves are lightly browned on top (approximately 25 minutes) and remove from the oven. Let the garlic cool until you can handle it (chill in freezer for 5 minutes if short on time) and then remove each clove from the bulb by pushing from the bottom of the clove and moving up. Set aside.

Sautéed Spinach Preheat a non-stick frying pan on medium heat and add the oil and then the onions. Sauté until lightly browned. Add the spinach and stir frequently. Sauté until the spinach has shrunken down. Add the roasted garlic and parmesan. **Serves 1 large or 2 small.**

Roasted Garlic

Garlic	**¼ cup**
Coconut oil or butter (melted)	**1 tbsp**

Sautéed Spinach

Olive oil	**1 tbsp**
Onion (small diced)	**¼ cup**
Spinach (tightly packed)	**6 cups**
Parmesan cheese (grated)	**¼ cup**
Salt	**2 pinches**
Pepper	**1 pinch**

Variations and Options

For a great anytime meal, serve with Stir-Fry Beef (pg.86). **For added flavor, sauté spinach with ¼ teaspoon ginger.** For a colorful nutrient boost, garnish with freshly chopped tomato. **To create a tasty omelet filling, make a double batch and use the mixture in your omelet.**

Coconut Cauliflower Mash

Ideal Pairing: Sirloin Burgers (pg.90)

At

Anytime
Meal

2
min.

Preparation
Time

15
min.

Cooking
Time

Nutritional Information

(per serving)	large	small
Calories (k/cal)	409.4	204.7
Fat (g)	27.3	13.6
Saturated (g)	13.3	6.7
Monounsaturated (g)	8.6	4.3
Polyunsaturated (g)	2.8	1.4
omega-3 (g)	0.0	0.0
omega-6 (g)	2.8	1.4
Carbohydrates (g)	27.8	13.9
fiber (g)	8.6	4.3
sugars (g)	9.2	4.6
Protein (g)	13.3	6.6

If you like mashed potatoes but worry about the high-carb content, worry no longer. Mashed cauliflower tastes just like mashed potato but has far fewer calories and packs a bigger nutrient punch. In this recipe, we've included a crunchy twist to mashed potatoes by adding cashews.

Instructions

Add all the ingredients to a pot and bring to a boil over medium heat. Reduce heat to low and cover with a tight-fitting lid. Simmer for 15 minutes and then remove from heat. Purée in a blender or food processor until smooth. Add 1 tablespoon of water at a time if necessary to get the mixture moving. **Serves 1 large or 2 small.**

Cauliflower (rough chopped)	**3 cups**
Cashews (crushed)	**¼ cup**
Coconut milk	**¼ cup**
Salt	**1 pinch**
Pepper	**1 pinch**
Cinnamon	**1 pinch**

Variations and Options

For a great anytime meal, serve with homemade Sirloin Burgers (pg.90). **For a great soup, add a cup of broth to this recipe when blending. Refer to page 266 for instructions on blending hot mixtures.** For additional flavoring, try adding your favorite herbs to the mash. Paprika, safflower, or coriander are awesome spices to try in this recipe. **If you don't have a food processor, you can mash with a fork.**

Miso Vegetable Brown Rice

Ideal Pairing: Salisturkey Steaks (pg.120)

Pw
Post-workout
Meal

10 min.
Preparation
Time

55 min.
Cooking
Time

Nutritional Information

(per serving)	large	small
Calories (k/cal)	468.2	234.1
Fat (g)	17.9	9.0
Saturated (g)	2.0	1.0
Monounsaturated (g)	3.6	1.8
Polyunsaturated (g)	11.1	5.5
omega-3 (g)	0.2	0.1
omega-6 (g)	10.7	5.3
Carbohydrates (g)	63.7	31.9
fiber (g)	8.8	4.4
sugars (g)	8.5	4.2
Protein (g)	13.0	6.5

Miso paste is an excellent addition to soups and broths as it adds a real flavor richness to an otherwise bland meal. Since this recipe uses broth to cook the rice, we decided to dress it up with miso. As miso is made by fermenting rice, barley, and/ or soybeans, these flavors complement each other well.

Instructions

Rinse the rice under cold water. Bring the broth to a boil in a medium-sized or large pot. Add the miso and stir until dissolved and then add the rice while stirring. Reduce heat to medium-low, cover and simmer for 45-55 minutes. Preheat a non-stick frying pan on medium heat, lightly coat with spray, add the mushrooms and sauté until they have shrunken a little. Then add the onion, zucchini and peppers and sauté for 3 minutes more. Now add 1 tablespoon of the broth from the cooked rice, and the ginger, and sauté for 1 minute more. Put the veggies and the cilantro into the rice and stir. **Serves 1 large or 2 small.**

Brown rice	⅓ cup
Vegetable broth	1 cup
Water	1 cup
Miso	1 tbsp
Olive oil cooking spray	
Mushrooms (quartered)	½ cup
Onion (small dice)	⅓ cup
Zucchini (halved and sliced)	⅔ cup
Red pepper (sliced)	¼ cup
Ginger (grated)	1 tsp
Sunflower seeds	¼ cup
Cilantro	1 tbsp

Variations and Options

For a great post-workout meal, serve with Salisturkey Steaks (pg.120). **For a great soup, double the broth.** For some veggie variety, choose brocccli, spinach and green beans as your veggie sources. **If you're not a fan of miso, it's ok. Simply eliminate it, or try replacing it with curry paste.**

Curry Coconut Chickpeas
Ideal Pairing: Lemon-Poached Cod (pg.154)

Pw

Post-workout
Meal

10 min.
Preparation Time

10 min.
Cooking Time

Nutritional Information

(per serving)	large	small
Calories (k/cal)	611.7	305.9
Fat (g)	35.6	17.8
Saturated (g)	29.4	14.7
Monounsaturated (g)	2.0	1.0
Polyunsaturated (g)	1.3	0.7
omega-3 (g)	0.0	0.0
omega-6 (g)	1.1	0.5
Carbohydrates (g)	58.9	29.5
fiber (g)	10.5	5.3
sugars (g)	6.5	3.3
Protein (g)	14.0	7.0

Chickpeas, or garbanzo beans, are high-protein, fiber-packed beans used in many curries and even in several condiments (such as hummus, for example). In this recipe, we've mixed together chickpeas, a host of veggies, and some curry powder to create a delicious curry meal that's really good for you too.

Instructions

Preheat a non-stick frying pan on medium heat, add coconut oil or butter and then add the napa cabbage. Sauté until cabbage shrinks down and add the onions and peppers and sauté for 2-4 minutes more. Add one tablespoon of the coconut milk and the garlic, ginger and curry powder. Sauté for 2 minutes more. Add the remaining coconut milk, chickpeas, salt and pepper and heat until warm. Add the fresh basil and serve. **Serves 1 large or 2 small.**

Coconut oil or butter	2 tsp
Napa cabbage or bok choy (sliced)	1 cup
Onion (small diced)	½ cup
Red pepper (small diced)	½ cup
Coconut milk (shake can very well first)	½ cup
Fresh garlic (minced)	1 tsp
Ginger (grated)	1 tsp
Curry powder	1 tsp
Chickpeas (cooked or canned, drained)	¾ cup
Salt	¼ tsp
Pepper	1 pinch
Fresh basil (thin sliced)	1 tbsp

Variations and Options

For a great post-workout meal, serve with Lemon-Poached Cod (pg.154). **For a great soup, add 1-2 cups of broth or low-fat milk. Season to taste, reheat and serve with your favorite protein.** Add some veggie variety by incorporating broccoli, cauliflower, spinach and cooked squash.

Black Bean Spinach Sauté
Ideal Pairing: Sirloin Skewers (pg.92)

At — Anytime Meal

5 min. — Preparation Time

6 min. — Cooking Time

Here's another delicious dish that's rich in fiber and veggies, a sizzling sauté of spinach, tomatoes, garlic and black beans. For great taste and great health, it's a combo that can't be beat.

Nutritional Information

(per serving)	large	small
Calories (k/cal)	416.6	208.3
Fat (g)	2.1	1.0
Saturated (g)	0.4	0.2
Monounsaturated (g)	0.1	0.1
Polyunsaturated (g)	0.6	0.3
omega-3 (g)	0.3	0.1
omega-6 (g)	0.3	0.2
Carbohydrates (g)	72.1	36.0
fiber (g)	26.5	13.3
sugars (g)	4.9	2.4
Protein (g)	27.4	13.7

Instructions

Preheat a non-stick frying pan on medium heat, lightly coat with spray, add half the spinach and sauté until wilted. Add the second half, and once it has wilted, add the onion, garlic and chili powder and sauté for 2 minutes more. Add the tomato and black beans and heat until warm. Season with salt and pepper and serve. **Serves 1 large or 2 small.**

Olive oil cooking spray	
Baby spinach or chopped spinach leaves (tightly packed)	4 cups
Red onion (sliced)	¼ cup
Fresh garlic (minced)	2 tsp
Chili powder	¼ tsp
Vine-ripened tomato (small dice)	½ cup
Black beans (cooked or canned, drained, 1 can)	1½ cups
Salt	½ tsp
Pepper	¼ tsp

Variations and Options

For a great post-workout meal, serve with Sirloin Skewers (pg.92). **To create a tasty soup, add 1-2 cups of broth along with sautéed chicken breast.** To create a tasty wrap, add chicken and low-fat cheese and then wrap in a whole wheat tortilla. **You can garnish this dish with low-fat plain yogurt as a great substitute for sour cream. Salsa and guacamole are great additions to this recipe too.** You can substitute black beans with kidney beans if you want a little change of pace.

Soy Ginger Lentils with Baby Bok Choy

Ideal Pairing: Marinated Tuna Steak (pg.158)

Pw
Post-workout Meal

5 min.
Preparation Time

30 min.
Cooking Time

Lentils are a member of the legume family and were, in fact, one of the first domesticated crops in the near east. With 26% protein, lentils are trumped only by soybeans as the highest protein plant foods. In this veggie-friendly recipe, lentils are prepared with ginger, bok choy, and corn to provide a host of delicious and nutritious ingredients.

Nutritional Information

(per serving)	large	small
Calories (k/cal)	562.4	281.2
Fat (g)	21.8	10.9
Saturated (g)	16.3	8.1
Monounsaturated (g)	3.0	1.5
Polyunsaturated (g)	0.9	0.5
omega-3 (g)	0.0	0.0
omega-6 (g)	0.2	0.1
Carbohydrates (g)	72.7	36.4
fiber (g)	13.1	6.6
sugars (g)	6.6	3.3
Protein (g)	18.9	9.5

Instructions

Bring water to a boil, add the lentils and stir well. Bring back to a boil, reduce heat to medium-low and cover. Simmer for 25 minutes or until lentils are at desired firmness. Drain excess water and set aside. Preheat a non-stick frying pan on medium heat. Add the butter, shallots, ginger, and bok choy and sauté for 1 minute. Add the corn, cooked lentils and soy sauce and stir until combined. Serve and enjoy. **Serves 1 large or 2 small.**

Water	2 cups
French green lentils (or red lentils)	½ cup
Butter	1 tbsp
Shallots (thin sliced)	2 tbsp
Ginger	1 tsp
Bok choy (sliced)	2 cups
Corn (frozen)	½ cup
Tamari soy sauce	1 tbsp

Variations and Options

For an excellent post-workout meal, serve with Marinated Tuna Steak (pg.158). **For a tasty soup, add 1-2 cups of broth or low-fat milk. Season to taste, reheat and serve with your favorite protein.** Be sure you choose French green lentils over regular green lentils. Further, if French are unavailable, choose red lentils instead. If you do make this swap, though, shorten your cooking time to 6 minutes.

Roasted Garlic Barley Risotto

Ideal Pairing: Baked Chicken Strips (pg.114)

Post-workout
Meal

5 min.
Preparation Time

30 min.
Cooking Time

Nutritional Information

(per serving)	large	small
Calories (k/cal)	562.4	281.2
Fat (g)	21.8	10.9
Saturated (g)	16.3	8.1
Monounsaturated (g)	3.0	1.5
Polyunsaturated (g)	0.9	0.5
omega-3 (g)	0.0	0.0
omega-6 (g)	0.2	0.1
Carbohydrates (g)	72.7	36.4
fiber (g)	13.1	6.6
sugars (g)	6.6	3.3
Protein (g)	18.9	9.5

Risotto is a flavorful Italian dish made with a base of rice. In this recipe, we decided to replace the rice with barley, a low-glycemic, fiber-rich cereal grain that's arguably better for you. Although some Italians would shudder to think of Risotto made without rice, we guarantee that you won't miss it at all. The rich taste of barley, the added veggies and the classic spicing will leave you a raving fan of this version.

Instructions

Preheat a medium-sized pot to medium-high heat and add the oil, onions and carrots. Sauté for 2 minutes and then add the barley. Sauté for 2 minutes more, stirring frequently. Add the vegetable broth, water, thyme and pepper and bring to a boil. Cover with a tight-fitting lid and reduce to low. Simmer for 25-30 minutes until most of the water is absorbed. Now add the roasted garlic and cheese and stir until cheese is melted. Serve and enjoy. **Serves 1 large or 2 small.**

Coconut oil or butter	1 tbsp
Onion (finely diced)	½ cup
Carrots (peeled, finely diced)	¼ cup
Pearl or pot barley	⅓ cup
Vegetable broth or water	1 cup
Water	½ cup
Thyme (dried)	¼ tsp
Ground pepper	¼ tsp
Roasted garlic (recipe on pg.194, finely diced)	¼ cup
Parmesan cheese (grated)	¼ cup

Variations and Options

For a great post-workout meal, serve with Baked Chicken Strips (pg.114). **For a tasty soup, add 1-2 cups low-fat milk. Season to taste, reheat and serve with your favorite protein.** If you like your risotto softer, add an extra ½ cup of water to the vegetable broth.

Fruity Cashew Quinoa

Ideal Pairing: Fruity Chicken Skewers (pg.116)

Pw

Post-workout
Meal

5 min.
Preparation
Time

20 min.
Cooking
Time

Nutritional Information

(per serving)	large	small
Calories (k/cal)	580.2	290.1
Fat (g)	20.1	10.1
Saturated (g)	3.2	1.6
Monounsaturated (g)	9.5	4.7
Polyunsaturated (g)	4.7	2.3
omega-3 (g)	0.1	0.1
omega-6 (g)	4.5	2.3
Carbohydrates (g)	82.0	41.0
fiber (g)	9.0	4.5
sugars (g)	11.8	5.9
Protein (g)	17.8	8.9

Quinoa has earned the title of super-grain for its low glycemic index, high fiber and complete protein content, rich vitamin and mineral profile, and gluten-free composition. In fact, quinoa is such a super-food that it's been heavily researched for use in long-duration manned spaceflights by NASA. Even if you're not going to the moon, you'll appreciate this out-of-this-world quinoa recipe – complete with fruits and nuts.

Instructions

Rinse quinoa in a fine strainer and drain. Bring veggie broth or water to a boil in a medium-sized pot and then add the rinsed quinoa. Cover with a tight-fitting lid and reduce heat to low. Simmer for 10 minutes and then add the apple, orange and cashews. Remove from heat and let it sit for another 10 minutes with the lid on. Add the cilantro, stir all the ingredients together and serve. **Serves 1 large or 2 small.**

Quinoa	½ cup
Vegetable broth	1 cup
Apple (core removed, small diced)	¼
Orange (peeled with outer and central white membrane removed, chopped)	¼
Raw cashews (chopped)	¼ cup
Fresh cilantro (chopped)	1 tbsp

Variations and Options

For a great post-workout meal, serve with Fruity Chicken Skewers (pg.116). **For a little variety, substitute cilantro with mint for a burst of refreshing flavor.**

Chunky Tomato Spelt

Ideal Pairing: Garlic Sautéed Prawns (pg.150)

Pw

Post-workout
Meal

3 min.
Preparation Time

60 min.
Cooking Time

Spelt is a low-gluten cousin of wheat that's often less heavily processed than most store-bought wheat varieties. For that reason, and because folks with wheat intolerance can enjoy it, we've created a delicious spelt recipe, which when added as a side to Garlic Sautéed Prawns really shines.

Nutritional Information

(per serving)	large	small
Calories (k/cal)	219.9	109.9
Fat (g)	1.3	0.7
Saturated (g)	0.2	0.1
Monounsaturated (g)	0.1	0.1
Polyunsaturated (g)	0.5	0.2
omega-3 (g)	0.0	0.0
omega-6 (g)	0.0	0.0
Carbohydrates (g)	42.1	21.0
fiber (g)	5.6	2.8
sugars (g)	10.9	5.5
Protein (g)	9.9	4.9

Instructions

Drain soaking water from the spelt. Bring fresh water to a boil in a medium-sized or large pot, add the spelt and stir. Cover and reduce heat to medium-low and simmer for 60 minutes. Remove from heat and strain any excess water. Combine the cooked spelt, tomato sauce, fresh tomato, green onion, salt, pepper, cinnamon, and spices in a pot and warm. **Serves 1 large or 2 small.**

Spelt (soaked over night in the fridge)	½ cup
Water	2 cups
Tomato sauce	¾ cup
Tomato (diced)	½ cup
Green onion	¼ cup
Salt	⅛ tsp
Pepper	1 pinch
Parsley (dried)	1 pinch
Cilantro (dried)	1 pinch
Rosemary (fresh)	1 pinch
Thyme (fresh)	1 pinch
Basil (fresh)	1 pinch

Variations and Options

For a great post-workout meal, serve with Garlic Sautéed Prawns (pg.150). **For an excellent soup, add 1-2 cups of broth or low-fat milk. Season to taste, reheat and serve with your favorite protein.** For a veggie boost, add your favorite vegetables or whatever is in season. **One pinch of cinnamon is also an amazing addition to this dish.**

Chickpea Cakes

Ideal Pairing: Roast Chicken Breast (pg.118)

Pw

Post-workout
Meal

10 min.
Preparation
Time

20 min.
Cooking
Time

Nutritional Information

(per serving)	large	small
Calories (k/cal)	484.2	242.1
Fat (g)	12.6	6.3
Saturated (g)	5.7	2.8
Monounsaturated (g)	2.3	1.1
Polyunsaturated (g)	2.1	1.0
omega-3 (g)	0.5	0.3
omega-6 (g)	1.6	0.8
Carbohydrates (g)	66.6	33.3
fiber (g)	12.6	6.3
sugars (g)	8.7	4.4
Protein (g)	26.1	13.1

Here's another great chickpea recipe that really takes advantage of the chickpea's high protein and fiber content while adding some great veggies and spices. These chickpea cakes are really tasty on their own as a snack or paired up with a meat source like Roast Chicken Breast.

Instructions

Preheat a non-stick frying pan on medium heat. Spray with cooking spray, add the red pepper, zucchini and onion, and sauté until lightly browned. Add oil, garlic, ginger and curry powder, and sauté for 1 minute more. Now add mixture to a blender or food processor along with the chickpeas, eggs, salt, pepper and lemon juice. Purée to a semi-smooth consistency. With frying pan on medium heat, spray with olive oil and scoop ⅙th of the mixture into the pan. Shape roughly into disks with the spoon. Repeat process, leaving some room between each cake, and cook until lightly browned (about 4 minutes). Carefully flip the cakes to brown the other side. Remove, set aside, and repeat until all cakes are cooked. Plate up the chickpea cakes and garnish with yogurt. **Serves 1 large or 2 small.**

Olive oil cooking spray	
Red pepper (rough chopped)	¼ cup
Zucchini (rough chopped)	¼ cup
Onion (rough chopped)	¼ cup
Coconut oil or butter	1 tsp
Fresh garlic (minced)	1 tsp
Ginger (grated or minced)	½ tsp
Curry powder	½ tbsp
Chickpeas (cooked or canned, drained)	1 cup
Whole egg	1
Egg white	1
Salt	¼ tsp
Pepper	2 pinches
Lemon juice	2 tsp
Low-fat plain yogurt	⅓ cup

Variations and Options

For a great post-workout meal, serve with Roast Chicken Breast (pg.118). **You can serve these as appetizers by cutting into quarters and garnishing with your favorite condiment.**

Vegetable Lentil Pâté

Ideal Pairing: Sautéed Chicken Breast (pg.112)

Post-workout Meal

10 min.
Preparation Time

60 min.
Cooking Time

Nutritional Information

(per serving)	large	small
Calories (k/cal)	557.5	278.8
Fat (g)	19.6	9.8
Saturated (g)	3.7	1.8
Monounsaturated (g)	7.5	3.8
Polyunsaturated (g)	7.9	4.0
omega-3 (g)	0.8	0.4
omega-6 (g)	6.2	3.1
Carbohydrates (g)	57.5	28.7
fiber (g)	23.7	11.9
sugars (g)	14.1	7.1
Protein (g)	37.8	18.9

Pâté is a traditional French dish made from minced and puréed meat (liver) and served with toast. As traditional pâté is very rich and quite fatty, we decided to create our own physique-friendly pâté with lentils, egg and veggies. Served crumbled on chicken or spread on a wrap, this dish is a great way to eat upscale and healthy at the same time.

Instructions

Bring water to boil in a small pot. Add lentils and cook for 25 minutes. Drain excess water. Set aside. Preheat oven to 350°F. Preheat a large non-stick frying pan on medium heat, coat with spray and add the mushrooms. Cook until the mushrooms have shrunken a little and then add the peppers, onions, garlic, salt, pepper, chili powder and turmeric. Sauté until lightly browned. Combine cooked veggies, egg, egg white and the cooked lentils in a blender or food processor and purée on low until the mixture is blended but still a little chunky. Transfer the mixture into a muffin tin greased with sesame seed oil. Fill almost to the top and place in the oven. Bake for 20-25 minutes or until firm to the touch. **Serves 1 large or 2 small.**

Water	1 cup
French green lentils	⅓ cup
Olive oil cooking spray	
Button mushrooms (sliced)	2 cups
Red pepper (large diced)	½ cup
Red onion (small diced)	½ cup
Garlic (minced)	2 cloves
Salt	1 tsp
Pepper	½ tsp
Chili powder	½ tsp
Turmeric	½ tsp
Whole omega-3 egg	1
Egg whites	2
Sesame seed oil	1 tbsp

Variations and Options

For a great anytime meal, crumble the pâté and combine with Sautéed Chicken Breast (pg.112). **You can add this pâté to a wrap with some vegetables and garnish with your favorite condiment (refer to Condiment chapter).** For some veggie variety, try substituting with zucchini, squash, carrots, celery or adding fresh herbs. Take note that you need about 1 cup sautéed veggies to 1 cup cooked lentils. **For some texture variety, add ¼ cup of your favorite chopped nuts.**

10

Snacks

There's a reason why protein bars are such big sellers in the nutritional supplement world and why granola bars are big sellers in the grocery store world – they're quick and convenient snacks that folks can eat on the go.

Unfortunately, though, most of the popular granola bars are too low in protein and too high in sugar to qualify as healthy meal replacements or even as healthy snacks. Even the protein bars sold in most health food stores are basically candy bars with some added protein (and often a bunch of unnatural, unhealthy chemical ingredients).

But don't worry – *Gourmet Nutrition* is here to save the day. In this section we've provided a series of high-protein snacks and bars that even the busiest of folks can quickly grab and enjoy on the run.

These recipes are perfect for meals on the go or for snacking between meals. Just don't make the mistake of replacing too many of your meals with snacks and bars. Even though they use mostly healthy, unprocessed ingredients, you still need a variety of whole food sources to engineer your own healthy diet.

Banana Nut Squares

		10 min.	10 min.
Anytime Meal	Post-workout Meal	Preparation Time	Cooking Time

Nutritional Information

(per serving)	large	small
Calories (k/cal)	568.8	284.4
Fat (g)	29.8	14.9
Saturated (g)	2.8	1.4
Monounsaturated (g)	4.0	2.0
Polyunsaturated (g)	19.4	9.7
omega-3 (g)	3.7	1.8
omega-6 (g)	15.7	7.9
Carbohydrates (g)	29.3	14.7
fiber (g)	6.6	3.3
sugars (g)	3.7	1.8
Protein (g)	45.8	22.9

Banana-nut breads are popular worldwide for their delicious combination of banana and walnut flavors as well as their starchy and nutty textures. While this version of Banana Nut Squares isn't quite the same as your grandma's, it still tastes awesome and is likely lower in fat, lower in carbs, and higher in protein. Wait until the smell of this recipe permeates your kitchen.

Instructions

Preheat oven to 350°F. Whisk the eggs and then combine with cottage cheese and banana. Combine the oats, walnut meal, protein powder, baking soda and salt and stir until evenly mixed. Slowly add the egg/banana mix to the dry ingredients until incorporated. Lightly coat a 9 by 9 inch baking pan with spray and then transfer mixture into the pan. Bake for 10-15 minutes (or until a toothpick comes out clean from the edges). Be careful not to over-bake as the squares will dry out. Cool, portion and store in the fridge or freezer, individually wrapped.
Serves 4 large or 8 small.

Banana (very ripe, mashed)	**½ cup**
Whole omega-3 eggs	**2**
Cottage cheese	**¼ cup**
Rolled oats	**½ cup**
Walnut meal	**2 cups**
Vanilla protein powder (equal to 150 g)	**6 scoops**
Baking soda	**¼ tsp**
Salt	**⅛ tsp**
Olive oil cooking spray	

Variations and Options
For a more nutty texture, add in ¼ cup crushed nuts.

Pumpkin Pie Bars

Pw
Post-workout
Meal

10 min.
Preparation
Time

25 min.
Cooking
Time

Nutritional Information

(per serving)	large	small
Calories (k/cal)	710.0	355.0
Fat (g)	29.0	14.5
Saturated (g)	17.0	8.5
Monounsaturated (g)	1.5	0.8
Polyunsaturated (g)	0.5	0.3
omega-3 (g)	0.2	0.1
omega-6 (g)	0.3	0.2
Carbohydrates (g)	77.0	38.5
fiber (g)	8.0	4.0
sugars (g)	39.0	19.5
Protein (g)	37.0	18.5

Here's a new take on pumpkin pie – high protein pumpkin bars. These bars are so good you won't want to eat traditional pumpkin pie ever again.

Instructions

Preheat oven to 350°F. Combine oats, flour and brown sugar in a mixing bowl and stir to combine. Add the cubed butter to the bowl and squeeze into the other ingredients using your hands until a coarse breadcrumb-like texture is achieved and everything is combined. Transfer ingredients into a 9 by 13 inch baking pan and press down. Place in oven and bake for 12 minutes. In the meantime, bring milk to a boil with the cinnamon, nutmeg and salt. As soon as it boils, transfer to a large mixing bowl. Stir in the pumpkin first and then the protein powder and eggs. If necessary, sweeten mixture to taste with Splenda®. Once the base has finished baking, remove from the oven and pour the pumpkin filling on top. Place back in the oven and bake for 20 minutes or until pumpkin filling has set. It should be a little firm to the touch. Cool, portion and store in the fridge or freezer, individually wrapped. **Serves 4 large or 8 small.**

Base

Quick cooking oats	½ cup
Whole wheat flour	1 cup
Brown sugar (packed)	½ cup
Cold butter (small cubed)	½ cup

Filling

Low-fat/skim milk	2 cups
Cinnamon	1½ tsp
Nutmeg	1 tsp
Salt	½ tsp
Pumpkin purée (canned)	2 cups
Vanilla protein powder (equal to 125 g)	5 scoops
Whole omega-3 eggs (beaten)	3
Splenda®, to taste	

Variations and Options

If you are lactose intolerant or wish to avoid dairy, replace the 2 cups milk with 2 cups non-cow's-milk dairy (e.g. goat's milk).

Peanut Crunch Bars

At

Anytime
Meal

10
min.

Preparation
Time

If you're addicted to peanut butter, like we are, you'll absolutely love these peanut crunch bars. They're chewy, creamy and chunky – all in the same bite. Just be careful, you might not be able to eat just one.

Pure honey	1 tbsp
Pure vanilla extract	1 tsp
Low-fat cottage cheese	½ cup
Cinnamon	½ tsp
Water	¼ cup
All natural peanut butter (chunky)	1 cup
Vanilla protein powder (equal to 125 g)	5 scoops
Oat flour	½ cup
Almonds (sliced)	¼ cup

Nutritional Information

(per serving)	large	small
Calories (k/cal)	747.0	373.5
Fat (g)	44.1	22.1
Saturated (g)	6.2	3.1
Monounsaturated (g)	21.9	11.0
Polyunsaturated (g)	12.0	6.0
omega-3 (g)	0.1	0.0
omega-6 (g)	11.9	6.0
Carbohydrates (g)	34.3	17.1
fiber (g)	9.4	4.7
sugars (g)	11.6	5.8
Protein (g)	53.2	26.6

Instructions

Add the honey, vanilla, cottage cheese, cinnamon and water to a food processor or blender and purée until smooth. Transfer to a mixing bowl along with the peanut butter. Stir to combine. Add the protein powder and stir to combine (this may take a minute). Add the oat flour and stir to combine again. Using a baking pan (9 by 9 inch) for measurement, pull out a piece of plastic wrap about 2 times the length of the pan. Then cover the baking pan with the wrap, allowing the extra plastic length to hang over the edge of the pan. Scoop the mixture above onto the plastic wrap inside the baking pan. Next, lift the corners of the extra plastic wrap and fold over the top of the mixture. Spread out the mixture with a spatula, making sure it fills the pan and that there's a layer of plastic wrap above and below the bars. Next, uncover the top of the bars and press the sliced almonds into the top of the bars. Chill in refrigerator for 2 hours. For a large bar, cut into approximately 4 by 4 inch pieces, and for a small serving cut into 2 by 2 inch bars. **Serves 4 large or 8 small.**

Variations and Options

If you are lactose intolerant or wish to avoid dairy, replace the ½ cup cottage cheese with ½ cup plain, lactose-free yogurt. Alternatively, you can replace with non-cow's-milk dairy (e.g. goat's milk). **You can make your own oat flour by adding rolled oats to a food processor and pulsing until a fine grainy flour is achieved.** If you like a smoother bar, choose smooth peanut butter. If you like a chunkier bar, choose chunky. **For some variety, replace the peanut butter with almond butter.** **Pw** option: Add some mini marshmallows and chocolate chips for a peanut smore bar.

Gooey Chocolate Chip Muffins

Pw
Post-workout
Meal

10 min.
Preparation
Time

10 min.
Cooking
Time

Nutritional Information

(per serving)	large	small
Calories (k/cal)	557.9	278.9
Fat (g)	25.4	12.7
Saturated (g)	16.0	8.0
Monounsaturated (g)	4.2	2.1
Polyunsaturated (g)	0.9	0.5
omega-3 (g)	0.1	0.0
omega-6 (g)	0.8	0.4
Carbohydrates (g)	52.5	26.3
fiber (g)	5.7	2.8
sugars (g)	18.8	9.4
Protein (g)	30.0	15.0

Everybody loves chocolate chip muffins. So even though they're a decadent treat, we decided to create a GN version here, including a variety of ingredients designed to improve the overall nutritional profile of the classic muffin mix. Be forewarned, however. These muffins are still high in calories and carbs. So you'll want to make sure to earn them in the gym and eat them post-exercise.

Instructions

Preheat oven to 350°F. Put all ingredients together in a mixing bowl and stir with a wooden spoon until combined. Lightly coat a non-stick muffin pan with spray and fill each muffin tin almost to the top. Place in the oven and bake 10 minutes or until the top is set. Cool, and store in the freezer, individually wrapped. **Serves 6 large or 12 small.**

Unsalted butter (room temperature)	½ cup
Whole omega-3 eggs	4
Coconut milk	¼ cup
Pure vanilla extract	1 tsp
Whole wheat flour	2 cups
Chocolate protein powder (equal to 150 g)	6 scoops
Cocoa powder	1 tbsp
Baking powder	1 tsp
Splenda® (1 package)	1 tsp
Chocolate chips	½ cup
Dried fruit (chopped)	½ cup

Variations and Options

You can substitute the dried fruit in this recipe with seeds or crushed nuts. **For some additional healthy fat, slice and spread with natural almond or peanut butter.** Be sure to pair with a higher-protein meal or snack as this recipe is lower in protein.

Granola Bars

Pw
Post-workout Meal

10 min.
Preparation Time

15 min.
Cooking Time

We avoid store-bought granola bars like the plague, as they're often loaded with processed ingredients, sugar and artificial ingredients. So we decided to create our own Gourmet Nutrition Granola Bars to do it the healthy, body-friendly way.

Oats	3 cups
Cranberries	½ cup
Walnut meal	½ cup
Almonds (sliced)	⅓ cup
Coconut milk	⅓ cup
Pure honey	¼ cup
Coconut (grated)	¼ cup
Olive oil cooking spray	

Nutritional Information

(per serving)	large	small
Calories (k/cal)	497.3	248.7
Fat (g)	22.7	11.4
Saturated (g)	6.8	3.4
Monounsaturated (g)	5.1	2.6
Polyunsaturated (g)	9.3	4.7
omega-3 (g)	1.4	0.7
omega-6 (g)	7.9	4.0
Carbohydrates (g)	60.0	30.0
fiber (g)	9.0	4.5
sugars (g)	19.0	9.5
Protein (g)	13.2	6.6

Instructions

Preheat oven to 350°F. Combine all ingredients in a mixing bowl and stir until incorporated. Lightly coat a 9 by 9 inch square pan with spray and transfer mixture to pan. Press the mixture down until flat and even and pushed into all corners. Bake for 12 or 20 minutes depending if you like it chewy or crisp. Cool, portion and store in the fridge or freezer, individually wrapped. **Serves 4 large or 8 small.**

Variations and Options

As this recipe is low in protein, you'll want to serve it along with a protein-rich snack. Our Blueberry Power Yogurt or Strawberry Coconut Pudding would make a great match. Or, for an even simpler protein boost, serve with cottage cheese or a protein shake. **For a lower-calorie option, use sugar-free maple syrup as a substitute for honey.** To boost the protein content of these bars, add 4-5 scoops of protein powder to the recipe, adding some water, 1 tablespoon at a time, until the mixture is wet but still sticky.

Apple-Cinnamon Bars

At

Anytime
Meal

10 min.
Preparation
Time

15 min.
Cooking
Time

Nutritional Information

(per serving)	large	small
Calories (k/cal)	688.4	344.2
Fat (g)	38.2	19.1
Saturated (g)	4.8	2.4
Monounsaturated (g)	21.7	10.9
Polyunsaturated (g)	7.6	3.8
omega-3 (g)	0.2	0.1
omega-6 (g)	7.4	3.7
Carbohydrates (g)	35.9	17.9
fiber (g)	9.4	4.7
sugars (g)	5.0	2.5
Protein (g)	50.2	25.1

Apples and cinnamon make an amazing flavor pairing, as you see in classic dishes like apple pie and apple crumble. If you're a fan of apples and cinnamon, you'll love this Apple-Cinnamon Bar. It tastes just like apple crumble but it's packed with natural ingredients and protein power.

Instructions

Preheat oven to 350°F. Mix the egg whites with the applesauce and beat for a minute. Mix the protein, cinnamon, salt, oats and nut meal. Slowly stir the egg white/applesauce mixture into the dry ingredients until totally incorporated and then stir the apple pieces in. Lightly coat a 9" by 9" inch baking pan with spray and transfer the mixture into the pan. Bake for 10-15 minutes until a toothpick inserted in the center comes out clean. Cool, portion and store in the fridge or freezer, individually wrapped. **Serves 4 large or 8 small.**

Egg whites	**2**
Unsweetened applesauce	**½ cup**
Vanilla whey protein (equal to 150 g)	**6 scoops**
Cinnamon	**¼ tsp**
Salt	**⅛ tsp**
Oats	**½ cup**
Nut meal (ground mixed nuts in blender)	**2 cups**
Apple (cubed)	**½ cup**
Olive oil cooking spray	

Variations and Options

For some fruit variety, substitute pears for apples in the recipe.

Blueberry Power Yogurt

Anytime
Meal

2
min.

Preparation
Time

Sometimes you just need a quick, two-minute snack before you head out the door. Well, here it is. This is a simple, great-tasting protein- and calcium-rich snack that can be eaten quickly between meals or as a dessert. Nothing fancy here – just healthy berries, yogurt and protein.

Plain low-fat yogurt	½ cup
Vanilla protein powder (equal to 25 g)	1 scoop
Blueberries (frozen)	2 tbsp

Nutritional Information

(per serving)	large	small
Calories (k/cal)	200.0	100.0
Fat (g)	1.8	0.9
Saturated (g)	0.2	0.1
Monounsaturated (g)	0.1	0.0
Polyunsaturated (g)	0.1	0.0
omega-3 (g)	0.0	0.0
omega-6 (g)	0.0	0.0
Carbohydrates (g)	15.8	7.9
fiber (g)	1.5	0.8
sugars (g)	11.1	5.5
Protein (g)	30.1	15.1

Instructions

Add the protein powder to the yogurt and stir until completely incorporated. Add the blueberries, stir and serve. **Serves 1 large or 2 small.**

Variations and Options

This simple recipe makes a great bedtime snack and can be paired with Poached Pears, Homemade Granola or the Wholesome Fruit Crumble. **If you are lactose intolerant or wish to avoid dairy, replace the ½ cup yogurt with ½ cup lactose-free yogurt. Alternatively, you can substitute with non-cow's-milk dairy (e.g. goat's milk).**

Strawberry Coconut Pudding

At

Anytime
Meal

2
min.

Preparation
Time

Pudding is a delicious snack staple that's typically high in sugar. We don't really "do" sugar, and neither should you. So we decided to create a low-sugar pudding recipe that's both delicious and good for you.

Low-fat cottage cheese	¾ cup
Coconut milk	¼ cup
Strawberries (frozen)	½ cup
Splenda®	¼ tsp

Nutritional Information

(per serving)	large	small
Calories (k/cal)	270.0	135.0
Fat (g)	16.0	8.0
Saturated (g)	13.8	6.9
Monounsaturated (g)	1.1	0.6
Polyunsaturated (g)	0.2	0.1
omega-3 (g)	0.0	0.0
omega-6 (g)	0.2	0.1
Carbohydrates (g)	11.3	5.6
fiber (g)	2.3	1.2
sugars (g)	8.0	4.0
Protein (g)	22.5	11.3

Instructions

Combine all ingredients in a blender or food processor and purée until smooth. This recipe is between a pudding and shake. To thicken, add a scoop of protein powder (strawberry or vanilla). To thin, add a little water at a time until desired consistency is reached. **Serves 1 large or 2 small.**

Variations and Options

If you are lactose intolerant or wish to avoid dairy, replace the ¾ cup cottage cheese with ¾ cup lactose-free yogurt. Alternatively, you can substitute with non-cow's-milk dairy (e.g. goat's milk). **Pw** **option: For an additional treat, serve this pudding on top of fresh chopped fruit, such as apple, banana, pears, or berries or along with a serving of Wholesome Fruit Crumble.** For some fruit variety, try substituting the strawberry with blueberry, blackberry or mango. **This simple recipe makes a great bedtime snack and can be paired with Poached Pears, Homemade Granola or the Wholesome Fruit Crumble.**

Homemade Granola

Pw
Post-workout
Meal

5 min.
Preparation
Time

25 min.
Cooking
Time

Nutritional Information

(per serving)	large	small
Calories (k/cal)	355.2	177.6
Fat (g)	21.7	10.9
Saturated (g)	10.5	5.2
Monounsaturated (g)	3.3	1.6
Polyunsaturated (g)	6.5	3.3
omega-3 (g)	1.1	0.6
omega-6 (g)	1.4	0.7
Carbohydrates (g)	32.0	16.0
fiber (g)	6.3	3.1
sugars (g)	6.4	3.2
Protein (g)	7.9	4.0

Granola is always a delicious snack treat typically loaded with healthy ingredients including oats, nuts and natural honey. However, commercial preparations of granola often contain a host of unhealthy additives and sugary ingredients. So we decided to go back to the basics with this excellent homemade granola. It's a recipe that you're sure to love.

Instructions

Preheat oven to 350°F and place the rack in the middle. Put all ingredients in a mixing bowl and stir until well combined. Place on a cookie sheet and bake in the oven, mixing once during baking until oats are golden brown (about 20 minutes). Then remove to cool. **Serves 5 large or 10 small.**

Old fashioned oats	**2 cups**
Walnuts (chopped)	**½ cup**
Cinnamon	**½ tsp**
Fennel seed (ground)	**½ tsp**
Maple syrup	**2 tbsp**
Unsweetened coconut	**¼ cup**
Coconut oil or butter (melted)	**2 tbsp**

Variations and Options

As this recipe is low in protein, you'll want to serve it along with a protein-rich snack. Our Blueberry Power Yogurt or Strawberry Coconut Pudding would make a great match. Or, for an even simpler protein boost, serve with cottage cheese or a protein shake. **For a nutty variety, try using pecans, cashews, almonds or a variety of seeds in place of walnuts.** For some added sweetness, dried fruit goes really well in granola, so add craisins, raisins, dried apples, dried bananas and more if you'd like to create a fruity granola.

Wholesome Fruit Crumble

Pw

Post-workout Meal

10 min.
Preparation Time

10 min.
Cooking Time

Nutritional Information

(per serving)	large	small
Calories (k/cal)	421.5	210.8
Fat (g)	9.2	4.6
Saturated (g)	4.3	2.1
Monounsaturated (g)	2.9	1.5
Polyunsaturated (g)	1.0	0.5
omega-3 (g)	0.1	0.1
omega-6 (g)	0.9	0.4
Carbohydrates (g)	78.9	39.4
fiber (g)	11.8	5.9
sugars (g)	38.9	19.5
Protein (g)	5.8	2.9

The natural sweetness of cooked fruit makes fruit crumbles a real favorite from kids to adults. This particular fruit crumble recipe minimizes the added sugar while maximizing the fruity goodness. As such, it can be eaten alone or in conjunction with a crunchy topping like our Homemade Granola.

Instructions

Preheat a large pot on medium heat. Add the oil, water, apples and pears. Cook until the fruit starts going soft (about 5-8 minutes) and then add the cinnamon, honey and vanilla extract and cook a few more minutes until the liquid is slightly thickened. Stir in the raspberries and remove from heat to cool a little. Add to ½ or ¼ cup Homemade Granola. **Serves 2 large or 4 small.**

Coconut oil or butter	1 tbsp
Water	2 tbsp
Gala apples (core removed, large chopped)	1 cup
Pears (core removed, large chopped)	1 cup
Cinnamon	½ tsp
Honey	2 tsp
Pure vanilla extract	½ tsp
Raspberries (frozen)	1 cup
Homemade granola (recipe on page 234 or use store-bought)	1 cup

Variations and Options

As this recipe is low in protein, you'll want to serve it along with a protein-rich snack. Our Blueberry Power Yogurt or Strawberry Coconut Pudding would make a great match. Or, for an even simpler protein boost, serve with cottage cheese or a protein shake. **This meal is versatile, so you can serve it warm or cold.** For some fruit variety, try substituting the raspberries with blueberries or blackberries.

Poached Pears

Post-workout Meal	5 min. Preparation Time	2 min. Cooking Time

Here's another simple, yet delicious snack recipe. Pears, honey, cinnamon and nuts – what's not to like about this one? Perfect when you're on the go.

Nutritional Information

(per serving)	large	small
Calories (k/cal)	476.2	238.1
Fat (g)	18.0	9.0
Saturated (g)	2.4	1.2
Monounsaturated (g)	10.8	5.4
Polyunsaturated (g)	3.8	1.9
omega-3 (g)	0.7	0.3
omega-6 (g)	3.7	1.9
Carbohydrates (g)	71.3	35.6
fiber (g)	13.4	6.7
sugars (g)	45.4	22.7
Protein (g)	7.2	3.6

Instructions

Combine all of the ingredients except pears in a mixing bowl. Evenly spoon mixture into the center of the four pears (where the core was removed). Place in a covered casserole dish or on a plate with plastic-wrap and microwave until pears begin to soften (approximately 2 minutes). Cool for a couple of minutes and serve. **Serves 2 large or 4 small.**

Cinnamon	**¼ tsp**
Honey	**2 tsp**
Pure vanilla extract	**½ tsp**
Mixed nuts (dry roasted, unsalted)	**¼ cup**
Pears (peeled, halved lengthways, core removed)	**2**

Variations and Options

As this recipe is low in protein, you'll want to serve it along with a protein-rich snack. Our Blueberry Power Yogurt or Strawberry Coconut Pudding would make a great match. Or, for an even simpler protein boost, serve with cottage cheese or a protein shake. **If you don't have a microwave or don't like to use them, then bake in a preheated 350°F oven for 10-15 minutes.** For some fruit variety, substitute the pears with apples.

11

Salad Dressings

For these salad dressings, add all ingredients to a blender or mini food processor and purée until everything is finely diced. If you don't have a blender or food processor handy, simply chop the veggies and herbs finely and incorporate all the ingredients together.

Orange Sesame Vinaigrette

Cold-pressed sesame seed oil	½ cup
Rice vinegar	¼ cup
Orange (peel, white stuff and seeds removed)	1
Pure honey	1 tbsp
Fresh mint (finely chopped)	¼ cup
Salt and pepper, to taste	

Serves 8 large or 16 small (A large serving = 4 tbsp; a small serving = 2 tbsp)

Nutritional Information

(per serving)	large	small
Calories (k/cal)	140.9	70.5
Fat (g)	13.6	6.8
Saturated (g)	1.9	1.0
Monounsaturated (g)	5.4	2.7
Polyunsaturated (g)	5.7	2.8
omega-3 (g)	0.0	0.0
omega-6 (g)	5.6	2.8
Carbohydrates (g)	4.5	2.2
fiber (g)	0.4	0.2
sugars (g)	3.7	1.8
Protein (g)	0.1	0.1

Balsamic Vinaigrette

Extra virgin olive oil	½ cup
Balsamic vinegar	½ cup
Shallots (finely diced)	¼ cup
Fresh parsley (finely chopped)	¼ cup
Salt and pepper, to taste	

Serves 8 large or 16 small (A large serving = 4 tbsp; a small serving = 2 tbsp)

Nutritional Information

(per serving)	large	small
Calories (k/cal)	125.1	62.6
Fat (g)	13.5	6.8
Saturated (g)	1.9	0.9
Monounsaturated (g)	9.9	4.9
Polyunsaturated (g)	1.4	0.7
omega-3 (g)	0.1	0.1
omega-6 (g)	1.3	0.7
Carbohydrates (g)	0.8	0.4
fiber (g)	0.0	0.0
sugars (g)	0.1	0.0
Protein (g)	0.1	0.1

Asian Dressing

Cold-pressed sesame seed oil	½ cup
Orange juice	½ cup
Shallots (finely diced)	¼ cup
Ginger (grated)	½ tsp
Fresh cilantro (finely chopped)	¼ cup
Salt, pepper and Splenda® to taste	

Serves 8 large or 16 small (A large serving = 4 tbsp; a small serving = 2 tbsp)

Nutritional Information

(per serving)	large	small
Calories (k/cal)	134.6	67.3
Fat (g)	13.7	6.8
Saturated (g)	1.9	1.0
Monounsaturated (g)	5.4	2.7
Polyunsaturated (g)	5.7	2.8
omega-3 (g)	0.0	0.0
omega-6 (g)	5.6	2.8
Carbohydrates (g)	2.6	1.3
fiber (g)	0.1	0.1
sugars (g)	1.3	0.7
Protein (g)	0.3	0.1

Mexi-Mix Dressing

Salsa	1 cup
Plain low-fat yogurt	1 cup
Flaxseed oil	¼ cup

Serves 8 large or 16 small (A large serving = 4 tbsp; a small serving = 2 tbsp)

Nutritional Information
(per serving)

	large	small
Calories (k/cal)	88.8	44.4
Fat (g)	6.9	3.5
Saturated (g)	0.7	0.3
Monounsaturated (g)	1.4	0.7
Polyunsaturated (g)	4.5	2.3
omega-3 (g)	3.6	1.8
omega-6 (g)	0.9	0.4
Carbohydrates (g)	4.4	2.2
fiber (g)	0.5	0.3
sugars (g)	3.3	1.7
Protein (g)	2.3	1.1

Caesar Vinaigrette

Extra virgin olive oil	½ cup
Lemon juice	¼ cup
Plain low-fat yogurt	¼ cup
Fresh garlic (minced)	1 tsp
Capers	1 tbsp
Dijon mustard	1 tsp

Serves 8 large or 16 small (A large serving = 4 tbsp; a small serving = 2 tbsp)

Nutritional Information
(per serving)

	large	small
Calories (k/cal)	128.5	64.2
Fat (g)	13.5	6.8
Saturated (g)	1.9	0.9
Monounsaturated (g)	9.9	4.9
Polyunsaturated (g)	1.4	0.7
omega-3 (g)	0.1	0.1
omega-6 (g)	1.3	0.7
Carbohydrates (g)	1.2	0.6
fiber (g)	0.0	0.0
sugars (g)	0.8	0.4
Protein (g)	0.5	0.2

Roasted Garlic Vinaigrette

Extra virgin olive oil	½ cup
Red wine vinegar	½ cup
Roasted garlic (recipe on pg.194)	¼ cup
Dijon mustard	2 tsp
Fresh cilantro (finely chopped)	¼ cup
Salt & pepper, to taste	

Serves 8 large or 16 small (A large serving = 4 tbsp; a small serving = 2 tbsp)

Nutritional Information
(per serving)

	large	small
Calories (k/cal)	132.9	66.4
Fat (g)	13.7	6.8
Saturated (g)	1.2	0.6
Monounsaturated (g)	3.1	1.6
Polyunsaturated (g)	8.6	4.3
omega-3 (g)	1.4	0.7
omega-6 (g)	7.2	3.6
Carbohydrates (g)	2.5	1.2
fiber (g)	0.4	0.2
sugars (g)	1.8	0.9
Protein (g)	0.0	0.0

Spicy Apple Vinaigrette

Walnut oil	½ cup
Apple cider vinegar	¼ cup
Organic gala apple (peeled, cored, cut into small pieces)	1
Paprika	1 pinch
Cinnamon	1 pinch
Salt and pepper, to taste	

Serves 8 large or 16 small (A large serving = 4 tbsp; a small serving = 2 tbsp)

Nutritional Information

(per serving)	large	small
Calories (k/cal)	132.9	66.4
Fat (g)	13.7	6.8
Saturated (g)	1.2	0.6
Monounsaturated (g)	3.1	1.6
Polyunsaturated (g)	8.6	4.3
omega-3 (g)	1.4	0.7
omega-6 (g)	7.2	3.6
Carbohydrates (g)	2.5	1.2
fiber (g)	0.4	0.2
sugars (g)	1.8	0.9
Protein (g)	0.0	0.0

Greek Vinaigrette

Extra virgin olive oil	½ cup
Red wine vinegar	½ cup
Shallots (finely diced)	¼ cup
Fresh basil (finely chopped)	¼ cup
Salt and pepper, to taste	

Serves 8 large or 16 small (A large serving = 4 tbsp; a small serving = 2 tbsp)

Nutritional Information

(per serving)	large	small
Calories (k/cal)	125.2	62.6
Fat (g)	13.5	6.8
Saturated (g)	1.9	0.9
Monounsaturated (g)	9.9	4.9
Polyunsaturated (g)	1.4	0.7
omega-3 (g)	0.1	0.1
omega-6 (g)	1.3	0.7
Carbohydrates (g)	0.8	0.4
fiber (g)	0.0	0.0
sugars (g)	0.1	0.0
Protein (g)	0.1	0.1

Caramelized Shallot Vinaigrette

Cold-pressed sesame seed oil	½ cup
Shallots (rough chopped)	¼ cup
Honey	1 tbsp
Balsamic vinegar	½ cup
Italian parsley (rough chopped)	¼ cup
Salt and pepper, to taste	

Preheat a non-stick frying pan or medium heat. Add 1 teaspoon of the oil, shallots and honey. Sauté until the shallots are nicely browned, and then add to the blender or mini food processor. Add the remaining ingredients and purée until shallots and parsley are chopped fine. **Serves 8 large or 16 small (A large serving = 4 tbsp; a small serving = 2 tbsp)**

Nutritional Information

(per serving)	large	small
Calories (k/cal)	146.6	73.3
Fat (g)	13.6	6.8
Saturated (g)	1.9	1.0
Monounsaturated (g)	5.4	2.7
Polyunsaturated (g)	5.7	2.8
omega-3 (g)	0.0	0.0
omega-6 (g)	5.6	2.8
Carbohydrates (g)	5.7	2.9
fiber (g)	0.0	0.0
sugars (g)	4.5	2.3
Protein (g)	0.2	0.1

Honey Mustard Dressing

Flaxseed oil	**½ cup**
Plain low-fat yogurt	**½ cup**
Garlic (minced)	**1 tsp**
Honey	**1 tbsp**
Dijon mustard	**1 tsp**
Paprika	**1 pinch**
Salt and pepper, to taste	

Serves 8 large or 16 small (A large serving = 4 tbsp; a small serving = 2 tbsp)

Nutritional Information

(per serving)	large	small
Calories (k/cal)	141.5	70.8
Fat (g)	13.9	6.9
Saturated (g)	1.4	0.7
Monounsaturated (g)	2.8	1.4
Polyunsaturated (g)	9.0	4.5
omega-3 (g)	7.3	3.6
omega-6 (g)	1.7	0.9
Carbohydrates (g)	3.4	1.7
fiber (g)	0.0	0.0
sugars (g)	3.2	1.6
Protein (g)	0.8	0.4

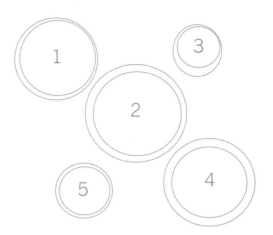

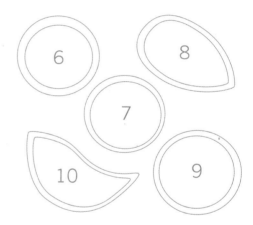

1. Orange Sesame Vinaigrette
2. Spicy Apple Vinaigrette
3. Balsamic Vinaigrette
4. Mexi-Mix Dressing
5. Asian Dressing
6. Honey Mustard Dressing
7. Caramelized Shallot Vinaigrette
8. Caesar Vinaigrette
9. Roasted Garlic Vinaigrette
10. Greek Vinaigrette

12
Condiments

One excellent way to jazz up any meal, including any meat, chicken or fish entrée, is to add some flavor in the form of a delicious condiment. If you choose wisely, the right condiments can really accomplish this goal without adding a bunch of unneeded calories to your daily intake.

But choosing wisely, especially at the grocery store, isn't always easy. Whether we're talking salsa, pesto, hummus or tzatziki, one thing is usually true: homemade condiments are typically lower in calories, contain less sodium, and have fewer processed or artificial ingredients than their store-bought counterparts.

So, by taking the reins yourself and preparing your own condiments in the comfort of your own kitchen, you'll now know exactly what's been added to your recipes. Plus, since you'll have control over all of the ingredients, you can tweak the recipes based on your own personal preferences.

When it comes to condiments, keep in mind that it's best to make larger batches and store them in smaller containers either in the fridge or freezer, based on how often you use them. Then, with these pre-prepared delicacies in hand, you can use them to quickly turn basic meals into gourmet meals by adding them to meats as a sauce, to salads as a dressing, to wraps as a garnish, and to sandwiches as a spread. And remember, these condiments are pleasantly potent – a little goes a long way.

So, in this section, we'll provide you with a number of condiments as well as some suggestions for appropriate meal pairings. Whether served as a side dish or a garnish, the variety of homemade condiments in this section is sure to please.

Rosemary Eggplant

Pairing: chicken, beef or seafood

10 min.
Preparation Time

10 min.
Cooking Time

Nutritional Information

(per serving)	large	small
Calories (k/cal)	60.5	30.2
Fat (g)	4.0	2.0
Saturated (g)	0.6	0.3
Monounsaturated (g)	2.6	1.3
Polyunsaturated (g)	0.5	0.3
omega-3 (g)	0.0	0.0
omega-6 (g)	0.5	0.3
Carbohydrates (g)	5.0	2.5
fiber (g)	1.5	0.8
sugars (g)	1.5	0.8
Protein (g)	1.3	0.6

Cooked eggplant takes on a rich, complex flavor that's a real treat for the palate. By spicing it up and using a base of yogurt to smooth it out, this delicious eggplant recipe offers a lot of utility. It can be used as a salad dressing, sauce or side dish. Further, it can replace mayonnaise in veggie dips, act as a garnish for crackers, and serve as a spread for wraps and sandwiches. Plus, it's much better for you than most dips and spreads.

Instructions

Preheat oven to 350°F. Preheat a large non-stick fry pan on medium heat. Add oil, water and then add the eggplant. Sauté, stirring every minute until lightly browned (about 5 minutes). Transfer to a casserole dish if necessary and bake for 10 minutes. Add eggplant back to the non-stick pan, add the shallots and rosemary, and sauté for 2 minutes more. Add the garlic and sesame seeds, and sauté for 1 minute more. Transfer to a mixing bowl and add yogurt, salt and pepper. Mash the mixture together with a fork until it begins to stick together. Let mixture cool and serve or store. **Serves 4 large or 8 small.**

Extra virgin olive oil	1 tbsp
Water	2 tbsp
Eggplant (large diced)	1 cup
Shallots (finely diced)	¼ cup
Fresh rosemary (finely chopped)	½ tsp
Fresh garlic (minced)	1 tsp
Sesame seeds	2 tsp
Low-fat plain yogurt	2 tbsp
Salt	¼ tsp
Pepper	⅛ tsp

Variations and Options

To use as a salad dressing, combine 2 parts spread with 1 part olive oil and 1 part balsamic vinegar. Serve as is or purée in a blender for a smooth dressing. **To use as a sauce, purée with a little coconut milk or regular milk and gently heat.**

Fresh Tomato Salsa

Pairing: eggs, chicken or beef

5-8
min.

Preparation
Time

Nutritional Information

(per serving)	large	small
Calories (k/cal)	50.9	25.4
Fat (g)	0.2	0.1
Saturated (g)	0.0	0.0
Monounsaturated (g)	0.0	0.0
Polyunsaturated (g)	0.1	0.1
omega-3 (g)	0.0	0.0
omega-6 (g)	0.1	0.1
Carbohydrates (g)	9.9	5.0
fiber (g)	2.6	1.3
sugars (g)	2.3	1.2
Protein (g)	2.3	1.1

We all know that tomatoes, with their rich lycopene content, offer a host of health benefits. Well, what better way to realize them than with this fresh Spanish-inspired salsa? This versatile dish can be used as a salad dressing, sauce, dip or garnish. It's delicious.

Instructions

Combine all ingredients in a mixing bowl and toss until well combined. Look at it for three minutes, while thinking "that was easy." Then serve or store. **Serves 3 large or 6 small.**

Vine-ripened tomato (small diced)	¾ cup
Red onion (finely diced)	¼ cup
Corn	¼ cup
Black beans (cooked or canned, drained)	¼ cup
Fresh garlic (minced)	1 tsp
Lime juice	1 tbsp
Fresh cilantro (chopped)	1 tbsp
Salt	1 pinch
Pepper	1 pinch
Chili powder	1 pinch

Variations and Options

To use as a salad dressing, combine 2 parts salsa with 1 part olive oil. Serve as is or purée in a blender for a smooth dressing. **To use as a sauce, serve cold or heat in a non-stick frying pan.** If you like the consistency of store-bought salsa more than the fresh, you can quickly sauté the onion, corn and garlic for 2 minutes. Then add the tomato and sauté for 5 minutes more. Add the rest of the ingredients and then serve or store. **If you like a more traditional salsa, omit the beans, and add finely diced red pepper.** To mix up the flavor, substitute garlic with ginger. **As in-season tomatoes are sweeter, if you're using out-of-season tomatoes, you can add Splenda® or stevia to taste.**

Almond Olive Tapenade

Pairing: chicken

5-8
min.
Preparation
Time

Nutritional Information

(per serving)	large	small
Calories (k/cal)	57.8	28.9
Fat (g)	5.4	2.7
Saturated (g)	0.7	0.3
Monounsaturated (g)	3.8	1.9
Polyunsaturated (g)	0.7	0.4
omega-3 (g)	0.0	0.0
omega-6 (g)	0.7	0.3
Carbohydrates (g)	1.6	0.8
fiber (g)	0.6	0.3
sugars (g)	0.1	0.1
Protein (g)	0.7	0.4

Olives really polarize the dinner table. Some folks absolutely love them while others can't stand the taste. If you're an olive lover, your mouth is probably watering already, just thinking about this tapenade. And if you're a health lover, you'll likely be pleased with the healthy fat content of the olive. Either way, this awesome dish can be served as a side dish, dip, salad dressing or sauce. It adds an amazing flavor burst to any meal.

Instructions

Combine all the ingredients in a blender or mini food processor and purée until combined. Mixture should still have a course texture. **Serves 8 large or 16 small.**

Kalamata olives (pitted, whole or sliced)	**½ cup**
Almonds (crushed)	**2 tbsp**
Shallots (peeled, rough chopped)	**2 tbsp**
Fresh garlic (peeled)	**1 clove**
Capers	**1 tsp**
Dijon	**1 tsp**
Fresh parsley (rough chopped)	**1 tbsp**
Pepper	**1 pinch**
Olive oil	**2 tbsp**

Variations and Options

To use as a salad dressing, whisk 1 part tapenade with 1 part olive oil and 1 part lemon juice. **This tapenade also makes an awesome filling for stuffed chicken breast or a spread for the top of a roast chicken breast.**

Spinach, Feta and Cashew Pesto

Pairing: vegetables, chicken, seafood or beef

10 min.
Preparation Time

Nutritional Information

(per serving)	large	small
Calories (k/cal)	52.6	26.3
Fat (g)	4.2	2.1
Saturated (g)	1.1	0.6
Monounsaturated (g)	2.2	1.1
Polyunsaturated (g)	0.5	0.3
omega-3 (g)	0.0	0.0
omega-6 (g)	0.5	0.2
Carbohydrates (g)	2.1	1.1
fiber (g)	0.4	0.2
sugars (g)	0.5	0.3
Protein (g)	1.7	0.8

Across the world, there are many forms of pesto, although the typical Italian pesto is made from a base of basil leaves, garlic and pine nuts. We decided to add our own unique flavor palate to this classic dish by choosing spinach, cashews and feta cheese as our base. Wait until you try it.

Instructions

Defrost the spinach and squeeze out all the water from it before measuring volume. Combine all the ingredients in a blender or mini food processor and purée until a grainy paste is formed. If more liquid is required, add another tablespoon of olive oil and lemon juice. **Serves 9 large or 18 small.**

Cooked spinach (frozen)	½ cup
Low-fat feta cheese	¼ cup
Cashews	¼ cup
Lemon juice	1 tbsp
Olive oil	1 tbsp
Cumin	1 pinch
Pepper (fresh ground)	1 pinch

Variations and Options

To use as a salad dressing, combine 1 part pesto with 1 part milk and 1 part olive oil. **To use as a sauce, add 1 cup veggie broth and heat gently in a pot. Serve with chicken, seafood or beef.** To use as a spread, simply spread on sandwiches and wraps. **You can also mix this pesto into a pan of sautéed veggies or on top of a cooked chicken breast.** If you'd like to use fresh spinach instead of frozen, simply sauté the spinach first. Three cups of fresh spinach will make about ½ cup cooked.

Sundried Tomato Tzatziki

Pairing: chicken or seafood

10 min.
Preparation Time

Nutritional Information

(per serving)	large	small
Calories (k/cal)	63.4	31.7
Fat (g)	0.9	0.5
Saturated (g)	0.5	0.3
Monounsaturated (g)	0.3	0.1
Polyunsaturated (g)	0.1	0.1
omega-3 (g)	0.0	0.0
omega-6 (g)	0.1	0.0
Carbohydrates (g)	10.3	5.2
fiber (g)	1.0	0.5
sugars (g)	8.8	4.4
Protein (g)	3.5	1.7

Tzatziki is a Greek appetizer that's often served as a sauce for souvlaki and gyros. Its smooth and cool yogurt and cucumber base makes it ideal for pairing with spicy dishes and hot spices. In this recipe, we've added our own flair to this classic appetizer by adding sundried tomatoes and a bit of honey.

Instructions

Combine all the ingredients in a blender or mini food processor and purée until desired consistency (you can leave it a little chunky or purée until totally smooth). **Serves 4 large or 8 small.**

Low-fat plain yogurt	**¾ cup**
Sundried tomatoes (rehydrated)	**¼ cup**
Cucumber (peeled, seeds removed, rough chopped)	**¼ cup**
Dried basil	**1 tbsp**
Pure honey	**2 tsp**
Fresh garlic (minced)	**1 tsp**
Salt	**⅛ tsp**
Pepper	**1 pinch**

Variations and Options

Served as is, this tzatziki makes a great dip for raw vegetables, a delicious salad dressing, or an awesome spread. It even goes great as a cold sauce with chicken or seafood.

Tomato Vegetable Chutney

Pairing: eggs, chicken, seafood or beef

10 min.
Preparation Time

10 min.
Cooking Time

This Indian-inspired dish is loaded with colorful veggies and is flavored with a unique combination of wine vinegar and honey – making this healthy recipe sweet and tangy. Served as a side dish, dip, sauce, spread or salad dressing, you'll love this tomato-based condiment.

Nutritional Information

(per serving)	large	small
Calories (k/cal)	45.7	22.8
Fat (g)	0.2	0.1
Saturated (g)	0.0	0.0
Monounsaturated (g)	0.0	0.0
Polyunsaturated (g)	0.1	0.0
omega-3 (g)	0.0	0.0
omega-6 (g)	0.0	0.0
Carbohydrates (g)	10.2	5.1
fiber (g)	1.0	0.5
sugars (g)	7.6	3.8
Protein (g)	0.8	0.4

Instructions

Preheat a large non-stick fry pan on medium heat and spray the pan. Add red onion, zucchini and yellow pepper and sauté until lightly browned. Add the garlic and sauté for 1 minute more. Now add the tomatoes, honey and vinegar and cook until most of the moisture has evaporated (approximately 5 minutes), stirring frequently. Remove from heat to cool. The chutney should be thick and chunky. Add the basil, salt and pepper. Serve at room temperature or chilled. **Serves 3 large or 6 small.**

Olive oil cooking spray

Red onion (small diced)	¼ cup
Yellow pepper (small diced)	¼ cup
Zucchini (small diced)	¼ cup
Fresh garlic (minced)	1 tbsp
Tomato (small diced)	1 cup
Pure honey	2 tsp
Red wine vinegar	2 tsp
Fresh basil (chopped)	1 tbsp
Salt and pepper, to taste	

Variations and Options

To use as a salad dressing, combine 2 parts chutney with 1 part olive oil. If you'd like the dressing to be smoother, purée in a blender. **To use as a sauce, serve cold or heat in a non-stick frying pan and serve on top of eggs, chicken, seafood or beef.** This dish also makes a great sauce for wraps, dip for raw vegetables, or garnish for eggs. **You could also add to a stir-fry for a tangy flavor boost.**

Yummy Hummus

Pairing: veggies and breads

Chickpeas (drained and rinsed)		1 cup
Fresh garlic		2 cloves
Sesame seeds		1 tbsp
Orange juice (fresh squeezed)		2 tbsp
Salt		¼ tsp
Pepper		⅛ tsp
Cumin		⅛ tsp
Extra virgin olive oil		2 tbsp
Fresh parsley (chopped)		1 tbsp

5-8 min.

Preparation Time

Hummus is a middle-eastern spread typically made of ground chickpeas, tahini, lemon juice and garlic. It's nutrient-rich, high in fiber, and makes for an awesome spread, dressing or sauce. In this recipe, we've added our own unique twist to the classic hummus by using sesame seeds and orange juice instead of tahini and lemon juice.

Instructions

Combine all the ingredients in a blender or mini food processor and purée until smooth. **Serves 10 large or 20 small.**

Nutritional Information

(per serving)	large	small
Calories (k/cal)	65.2	32.6
Fat (g)	3.6	1.8
Saturated (g)	0.5	0.2
Monounsaturated (g)	2.2	1.1
Polyunsaturated (g)	0.7	0.3
omega-3 (g)	0.0	0.0
omega-6 (g)	0.6	0.3
Carbohydrates (g)	6.3	3.1
fiber (g)	1.5	0.7
sugars (g)	1.1	0.6
Protein (g)	1.9	1.0

Variations and Options

Hummus makes a great dip for raw vegetables or a spread in wraps. **To add some extra flavor while reducing the strong garlic taste, substitute the fresh garlic with ½ cup roasted garlic (recipe on pg.194).** To make a curry hummus, add 1 teaspoon of curry powder. **For a great side dish, sauté 2 tablespoons of hummus with ½ cup of green beans.**

Tropical Fruit Salsa

Pairing: chicken or seafood

10
min.

Preparation
Time

Nutritional Information

(per serving)	large	small
Calories (k/cal)	49.1	24.5
Fat (g)	0.3	0.1
Saturated (g)	0.1	0.0
Monounsaturated (g)	0.0	0.0
Polyunsaturated (g)	0.1	0.0
omega-3 (g)	0.0	0.0
omega-6 (g)	0.1	0.0
Carbohydrates (g)	11.1	5.5
fiber (g)	2.2	1.1
sugars (g)	5.3	2.6
Protein (g)	0.6	0.3

Here's another salsa recipe to tickle your palate. Instead of a classic tomato base, this salsa uses a fruity base, making it a sweet pairing for many chicken and seafood dishes. Eaten on its own as a side dish, this salsa isn't too shabby either. Regardless of how you use it, this dish is a delicious addition to your fridge.

Instructions

Combine all ingredients in a mixing bowl and toss until mixed thoroughly. **Serves 3 large or 6 small.**

Tomato (finely diced)	½ cup
Mango (finely diced)	¼ cup
Strawberries (finely diced)	¼ cup
Pineapple (finely diced)	¼ cup
Apple (finely diced)	¼ cup
Lime juice (freshly squeezed)	2 tsp
Salt	⅛ tsp
Pepper	1 pinch
Chili powder	1 pinch
Fresh mint (finely sliced)	1 tbsp

Variations and Options

To use as a salad dressing, combine 2 parts salsa with 1 part olive oil and 1 part apple cider vinegar. **This salsa also makes an awesome complement to seafood and chicken.** To vary the recipe, try using your favorite fruits or whichever fruits are in season, local or fresh. Avocados, peaches and plums are a must-try variation.

Cooking Terms

Bake Cooking food by surrounding it with dry, heated air in a closed environment. The most common method is using an oven between 300°F and 400°F. Baking is the same as roasting; however, baking generally applies to fish, fruits, vegetables and grains and roasting to meats and poultry.

Blanch Very briefly and partially cooking food using boiling water or steam. If you want to freeze vegetables they should be blanched first to preserve freshness and quality.

Blend Mixing two or more ingredients together using a blender. Refer to recipe method for speed and blending times. Blending hot liquids should be done with extreme caution. Only fill the blender half full, put the lid on just before blending, and start on low and work up to high. When removing the lid lift it away from you.

Boil Cooking food in water that is very hot and turbulent. This method cooks food faster than poaching and simmering. Also, boiling refers to the process of heating liquid to the point of fierce bubbling.

Broil Browning or cooking the top layer using radiant heat from an overhead source. An oven turned to broil is most commonly used. The top element heats up and browns the food or melts the cheese. This process happens very quickly and does not work well for actually cooking food.

Caramelize The process of cooking sugars that gradually turns food brown and increases the sweetness. Sometimes additional sugar is added such as honey or brown sugar; however, you can also caramelize using the natural sugars found in fruits, vegetables and meats.

Chop Cutting food into smaller pieces where uniformity is not important. Rough chopped should result in fairly large pieces (approximately 1-inch squared) and finely chopped should result in very small pieces (as small as you can get it... within reason).

Combine Mixing two or more ingredients together using a wooden spoon, spatula or if you're in the mood, your hands. Ingredients should be evenly distributed.

Cube Cutting food into small somewhat uniform pieces, approximately ½ inch squared cubes unless otherwise specified.

Dice Similar to cubing food, dicing should result in smaller pieces approximately ¼ - ½ inch squared cubes.

Garnish Items, normally herbs, cheeses, sauces or spices, placed as finishing touches on a dish for a more appealing appearance and flavor.

Grate Cutting food into small pieces by running it up and down a sharp metal edge, such as a cheese grater.

Grill Grilling is similar to broiling except the heat source is located beneath the food. We suggest using a BBQ or frying pan for grilling. Medium to medium-high heat works best.

Marinate To soak food in seasoned liquids to add flavor. When meat is marinated for 2-8 hours, it should become more tender.

Mix See Combine.

Peel To remove the skin or outside covering of a vegetable or fruit using a peeler or by hand.

Pinch Approximately the same as an $\frac{1}{8}$ of a teaspoon; however, this is used when seasoning meats before cooking and exact measurements are not important. This is your opportunity to act like one of the pros.

Poach Cooking food in water over medium-low to low heat that is barely bubbling. Also, refers to the process of heating liquid (far below boiling) to the point that it is just barely bubbling.

Preheat Bringing a pan or oven up to temperature before using it to cook.

Purée See Blend. A puréed mixture should be completely smooth.

Roast Cooking food by surrounding it with dry, heated air in a closed environment. The most common method is using an oven between 300°F and 400°F. Roasting is the same as baking however, roasting generally applies to meats and poultry and baking to fish, fruits, vegetables and grains.

Reduce Cooking a liquid mixture over low heat to decrease its volume causing it to thicken and concentrate its flavors.

Sauté A cooking method that transfer heat from a hot pan to food using a small amount of hot oil/fat. In a professional kitchen, it's generally done quickly over high heat however, we suggest using a non-stick frying pan over medium heat to reduce the amount of fat required. Remember to stir frequently.

Simmer Cooking food in water over medium heat that is lightly bubbling. Compared to boiling, this method prevents covered liquid from boiling over. Also, simmering refers to the process of heating liquid (below boiling) to the point that it is gently bubbling.

Slice To cut food into long thin pieces.

Spray Refers to spraying.

Steam Cooking food via direct contact with steam. Food is placed in a steamer basket or rack above boiling water and then covered to trap the heat.

Stir Mixing ingredients together with a spoon or spatula. To prevent heated ingredients from burning, some recipes will make reference to stirring frequently or constantly.

Stir-fry Similar to sautéing, stir-frying is a cooking method that transfers heat from a hot pan to food using a small amount of hot oil/fat. In a professional kitchen, it's generally done quickly in a wok over very high heat stirring constantly; however, we suggest using a non-stick frying pan over medium heat to reduce the amount of fat required. Remember to stir frequently.

Whisk Mixing two or more ingredients together vigorously using a whisk or fork.

Recipes, Alphabetical Listing

Recipes by designation

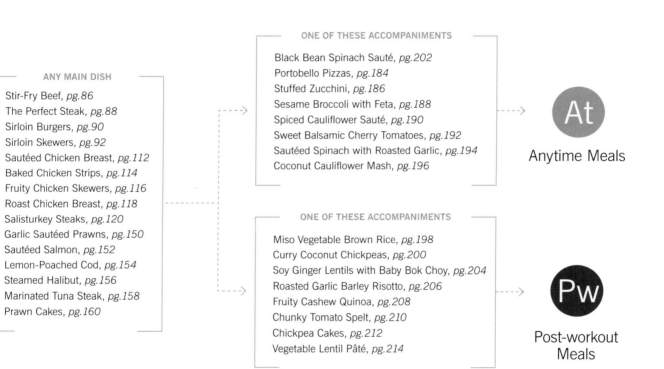

ANY MAIN DISH

Stir-Fry Beef, *pg.86*
The Perfect Steak, *pg.88*
Sirloin Burgers, *pg.90*
Sirloin Skewers, *pg.92*
Sautéed Chicken Breast, *pg.112*
Baked Chicken Strips, *pg.114*
Fruity Chicken Skewers, *pg.116*
Roast Chicken Breast, *pg.118*
Salisturkey Steaks, *pg.120*
Garlic Sautéed Prawns, *pg.150*
Sautéed Salmon, *pg.152*
Lemon-Poached Cod, *pg.154*
Steamed Halibut, *pg.156*
Marinated Tuna Steak, *pg.158*
Prawn Cakes, *pg.160*

ONE OF THESE ACCOMPANIMENTS

Black Bean Spinach Sauté, *pg.202*
Portobello Pizzas, *pg.184*
Stuffed Zucchini, *pg.186*
Sesame Broccoli with Feta, *pg.188*
Spiced Cauliflower Sauté, *pg.190*
Sweet Balsamic Cherry Tomatoes, *pg.192*
Sautéed Spinach with Roasted Garlic, *pg.194*
Coconut Cauliflower Mash, *pg.196*

At

Anytime Meals

ONE OF THESE ACCOMPANIMENTS

Miso Vegetable Brown Rice, *pg.198*
Curry Coconut Chickpeas, *pg.200*
Soy Ginger Lentils with Baby Bok Choy, *pg.204*
Roasted Garlic Barley Risotto, *pg.206*
Fruity Cashew Quinoa, *pg.208*
Chunky Tomato Spelt, *pg.210*
Chickpea Cakes, *pg.212*
Vegetable Lentil Pâté, *pg.214*

Pw

Post-workout
Meals

Post-workout Meals

About the Authors

About Dr. John M. Berardi

Dr. John M. Berardi is the President and Chief Science Officer of Precision Nutrition, a company devoted to translating exercise and nutrition research into real-world results.

Precision Nutrition provides nutrition and human performance consulting to sports teams at the professional, collegiate and Olympic levels, as well as individual consulting to athletes of all levels, from elite juniors right up to multiple gold medalists.

Through his website, www.precisionnutrition.com, Dr. Berardi and his team also offer fully-supported, distance-based body transformation coaching to men and women from all walks of life.

Dr. Berardi has written and lectured around the world on nutrition-related topics. He has authored or coauthored 5 books and over 200 articles in the popular press for magazines like *Men's Health, Men's Fitness, Women's Health, Muscle & Fitness, Testosterone* and others, and has been quoted in both the *New York Times* and *TIME Magazine*.

Dr. Berardi received his doctoral degree in exercise science from the University of Western Ontario, with a specialization in the areas of exercise biology and nutrient biochemistry. He is currently an adjunct assistant professor of Exercise Science at the University of Texas.

For more about Dr. Berardi, visit **www.precisionnutrition.com**

About Chef Michael Williams

Michael Williams often says that he became a chef by accident. Working for many years in family-style restaurants was always a job by necessity instead of a profession by choice. However, with natural talent on his side, he progressed quickly through the ranks and by the age of 21 was managing a staff of 40 people. Realizing that he had found his niche, he completed a 3-year apprenticeship in 6 months and received his Red Seal Chef Papers in 2001. Embarking on his professional career and knowing he'd need an edge on the other chefs in town, he pursued an opportunity to work at a 5-star hotel in Switzerland.

In the years since, Michael has worked at a number of top-class restaurants including the Relais & Châteaux Aerie Resort, voted #1 resort in North America (*Travel & Leisure Magazine 2006*). He was then invited to cook alongside Daniel Boulud at his renowned New York restaurant 'Daniel', and Michael Schlow, of Boston's 'Radius', after appearing on the hit television series "Making it Big." These experiences lead to Michael's first job as Executive Chef at an exclusive heli-ski resort in northern British Columbia, where he catered to an illustrious clientele.

Although Michael learned a lot as a professional chef, he has finally discovered his true calling, catering intimate in-home events and teaching everyday people from 9 to 90 years old how to create healthy yet delicious meals to enjoy with their family and friends.

For more about Michael Williams, visit www.chefmichaelwilliams.com

About Kristina Andrew

Kristina's passion for sports began at the age of three, when her 13-year career as a gymnast commenced. She trained at an elite level, working with coaches from all over the world, and attended workshops on athlete nutrition and training.

Although injury halted further aspirations as a gymnast, she took up two new sports, badminton and volleyball. Within a year she was competing provincially and continued on in volleyball, becoming an award-winning varsity athlete. In later years, she honed her skills in Rhode Island, USA and Rio de Janeiro, Brazil.

More recently, Kristina has worked as a personal trainer, a varsity level coach, and a cooking lesson instructor, alongside Chef Michael. Every day Kristina teaches the importance of healthy eating to her training clients, athletes, and cooking students. It's her mission to make people's lives in the kitchen easier, tastier and more fun.